The Construction of Buildings

Volume 3

By the same author
THE CONSTRUCTION OF BUILDINGS

Volume 1
Foundations, Walls, Floors & Roofs

Volume 2
Windows, Doors, Fires, Stairs and Finishes

Volume 4
*Foundations, Steel Frames, Concrete Frames,
Floors, Claddings*

Volume 5
Supply and Discharge Services
*Water Supply, Sanitary Appliances,
Sanitary Pipework Above Ground, Roof and
Surface Water Drainage, Drains Below Ground,
Electrical Supply, Gas Supply, Refuse Storage*

THE CONSTRUCTION OF BUILDINGS

Volume 3

SINGLE STOREY FRAMES, SHELLS AND LIGHTWEIGHT COVERINGS

OXFORD   LONDON   EDINBURGH

BOSTON   PALO ALTO   MELBOURNE

First published by Crosby Lockwood
    Staples 1972
Reprinted 1967
Second edition published by Granada
    Publishing in Crosby Lockwood Staples
    1972
Reprinted 1974, 1976, 1979
Reprinted by Granada Publishing 1981
Third edition 1984
Reprinted by Collins Professional and Technical Books 1987
Reprinted by BSP Professional Books 1988

British Library
Cataloguing in Publication Data
R. Barry
    The construction of buildings.—3rd ed.
    Vol. 3: Single storey frames, shells and
    lightweight coverings
    1. Building
    I. Title
    690   TH145

ISBN 0-632-02438-0

BSP Professional Books
A division of Blackwell Scientific
    Publications Ltd.
Editorial Offices:
Osney Mead, Oxford OX2 0EL
    (Orders: Tel. 0865 240201)
8 John Street, London WC1N 2ES
23 Ainslie Place, Edinburgh EH3 6AJ
3 Cambridge Center, Suite 208, Cambridge,
    MA 02142, USA
667 Lytton Avenue, Palo Alto, California
    94301, USA
107 Barry Street, Carlton, Victoria 3053,
    Australia

Set by Columns of Reading
Printed and bound in Great Britain by
Hollen Street Press, Slough

CONTENTS

NOTE ON METRIC UNITS

For linear measure all measurements are shown in either metres or millimetres. A decimal point is used to distinguish metres and millimetres, the figures to the left of the decimal point being metres and those to the right millimetres. To save needless repetition, the abbreviations 'm' and 'mm' are not used, with one exception. The exception to this system is where there are at present only metric equivalents in decimal fractions of a millimetre. Here the decimal point is used to distinguish millimetres from fractions of a millimetre, the figures to the left of the decimal point being millimetres and those to the right being fractions of a millimetre. In such cases the abbreviations 'mm' will follow the figures e.g. 302.2 mm.

R. BARRY

ACKNOWLEDGEMENTS

The illustrations in this volume have been redrawn by my friend Ross Jamieson, from my drafts.

Extracts from DD 73: 1982 shown in the table on page 49 are reproduced by permission of the British Standards Institution, 2 Park Street, London W1A 2BS from whom complete copies of the standard DD 73: 1982 can be obtained.

INTRODUCTION

The small-scale buildings described in Volumes 1 and 2 are constructed with traditional materials such as brick, timber, slate, tile and non-ferrous metals that have been used for centuries and have stood the test of time. The useful life of such buildings, if reasonably well maintained, is up to one hundred years or more.

This volume, Volume 3, describes the construction of single-storey buildings, such as factories, sports and leisure halls and other buildings generally built on one floor, which account for about 40% of the expenditure on building in this country.

Over the past fifty years most single-storey buildings have been constructed with a structural frame of steel or reinforced concrete supporting light-weight roof and wall coverings to exclude wind and rain and to provide insulation against loss of heat. The small imposed loads on roofs can be supported by thin, light-weight sheets fixed to comparatively slim structural frames to provide wide clear spans between internal supports. The thin, light-weight materials that are used for economy in weight and first costs, are not robust and do not withstand for long the destructive effects of weather, dimensional changes and damage in use that occur in buildings.

The consequence of the adoption of light-weight materials for roof and wall coverings, for the sake of economy, is that most single-storey buildings have a useful life of only twenty to thirty years before considerable works of repair or renewal are necessary to maintain minimum standards of comfort and appearance.

The concept of functional requirements for the elements of building is now generally accepted as a necessary guide to the performance criteria of materials and combinations of materials used in the construction of elements of building. In traditional building forms one material could serve several functional requirements, for example, a brick wall, which provides strength, stability, exclusion of wind and rain, resistance to fire, and, to some extent, thermal insulation.

The materials used in the construction of light-weight structures are, in the main, selected to perform specific functions. Steel sheeting is used as a weather envelope and to support imposed loads; layers of insulation for thermal comfort; thin plastic sheets for daylight; and a slender frame to support the envelope and imposed loads. The inclusion of one material for a specific function may affect the performance of another included for a different function which in turn may necessitate the inclusion of yet another material to protect the first from damage caused by the use of the second material, for example, where a vapour barrier is used to reduce condensation on cold steel roof sheeting.

Recently the demand for space heating and the consequent inclusion of materials with high thermal resistance has led to problems in building unknown to past generations who accepted much lower standards of heating and more ventilation of their homes and work places. The inclusion of layers of thermal insulation in the fabric of modern buildings, to meet current regulations and expectations of thermal comfort, has led to the destructive effects of condensation from warm moist air and also to the large temperature fluctuations of materials on the outside of insulation which has been one of the prime causes of the failure of flat roof coverings.

The use of thin, light-weight materials for the envelope of buildings has been for the sake of economy in first cost with little regard to the life of the building or subsequent maintenance or renewal costs. Where the cost of one material used in construction is compared to the cost of another, account should be taken of the relative costs of the elements of typical buildings as a measure of the value of the saving. A guide to the comparative cost of the elements of single-storey factory buildings is set out below.

Drainage and works below ground	25%
Structural frame	25%
Roofs and rooflights	20%
External walls and windows	15%
Heating, electrical and other services	15%

1

CHAPTER ONE

LATTICE TRUSS, BEAM, PORTAL FRAME AND FLAT ROOF CONSTRUCTION

The earliest mills, factories and warehouses were of traditional construction with brick or stone walls supporting timber framed roofs covered with slate or tile. The external brick or stone walls served as support for the roof and to exclude wind and rain. The limited span of a timber roof was adequate to the manufacturing process of the time, and the massive wall and heavy roof construction provided a durable structure with a useful life of one hundred years or more. The walls were constructed of solid brick or masonry generally stiffened and strengthened with piers to support the weight of the roof. There was an adequate supply of sound timber for the construction of the timber roof trusses that supported the traditional construction of purlins fixed across the trusses to support timber rafters, battens and slates or tiles. The timber trusses were framed with large-section timbers joined, strapped or bolted together for strength and rigidity. The two forms of timber truss in common use were the King post and Queen post truss.

Many of the early, traditional construction mills, factories and warehouses were built on several floors with internal cast iron columns giving intermediate support to single and double timber floors. Early mills and factories were artificially lit by oil lamps and heated by solid fuel burning stoves so that the hazard from fire was considerable. Modifications of the traditional construction, such as the iron beam and brick arch floor and iron and concrete floor, were introduced to reduce the risk of damage by fire.

The limited spans practicable with timber roofs and timber floors constrained the rapid expansion of manufacturing activity that was occurring during the nineteenth century to meet the demands of the rapidly increasing population of England and the very considerable export of finished goods.

The combination of the introduction of continuous hot-rolled steel sections in 1873, corrugated iron sheets in 1880 and corrugated asbestos cement sheets in 1910 led to the single-storey 'shed frame' form of construction for most new factories and warehouses. This 'shed frame' form of construction consisted of a light-weight frame of triangular roof trusses on brick side walls or steel columns covered with corrugated iron sheets or later with asbestos cement sheets fixed to small-section steel purlins and sheeting rails fixed across the roof and walls. This simple construction was economical in first cost in the use of materials, light in weight, easy to handle and quickly erected to provide the limited requirements of shelter expected of such small structures at the time. A symmetrical pitch single-bay shed frame is illustrated in Fig. 1. For many years the single-storey shed frame was the principal construction for small factories, warehouses and sheds to provide basic shelter for manufacturing, storage and agricultural purposes.

Natural lighting to the interior was provided by windows in the side walls and roof glazing in the form of timber or metal glazing bars fixed in the roof slopes to support glass. To avoid sun glare and overheating in summer the north light or 'saw-tooth' roof profile was introduced, a light section steel roof asymmetrical in profile with the steeply sloping roof fully glazed and facing north. A single-bay, north light shed frame is illustrated in Fig. 1.

With increase in the span of a triangular roof truss the volume of unused roof space and the roof framing increases and it is, therefore, of advantage to combine several bays of the shed frame construction to provide cover with the least volume of roof space and roof framing. To minimise the number of internal columns that would otherwise obstruct the floor, the 'umbrella' or cantilever roof was adopted. Lattice girders constructed at mid span in each bay support the trusses, and widely spaced internal columns in turn support the lattice trusses to provide maximum unobstructed floor space (Fig. 1).

The flat roof form of construction for single-storey factories and other wide span buildings was to a large extent for the sake of appearance. The lattice girder or beam grid on columns affords no advantage in unobstructed floor space or reduction in unused roof area over the umbrella form. The clean flat roof line and strong horizontal emphasis was accepted at the expense of many failures of flat roof coverings. In recent years improvements in materials and detailing of junctions have gone a long way to repair the ill-repute of flat roofs. A typical single-storey flat roof frame is illustrated in Fig. 1.

The plastic theory of design proposed by Professor Baker led to the use of the rigid steel portal frame for single-storey buildings. The rafters of the portal frame are rigidly connected to the posts in the form of a slender frame that is free of lattice members and can most economically have a shallow pitch suited to the profiled steel roofing or decking that came into production in about 1960. The majority of single-storey structures today are constructed with portal frames. Fig. 1 illustrates medium- and long-span portal frames.

Functional requirements
The functional requirements of framed structures are:

Strength and stability
Fire resistance.

2

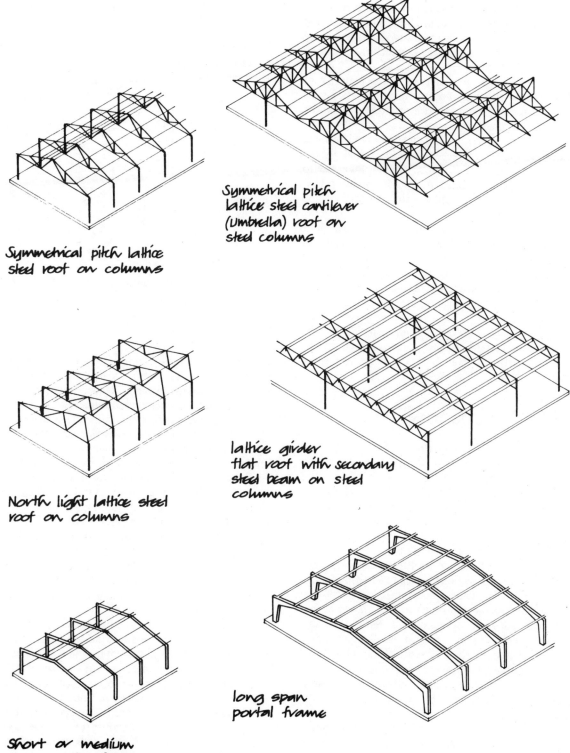

Symmetrical pitch lattice
steel roof on columns

Symmetrical pitch
lattice steel cantilever
(umbrella) roof on
steel columns

North light lattice steel
roof on columns

lattice girder
flat roof with secondary
steel beam on steel
columns

Short or medium
span portal frame

long span
portal frame

Typical Lattice and Portal frame construction

Fig. 1

Strength and stability: The strength of a structural frame depends on the material used in the manufacture and fabrication of the members of the frame and the stability of the frame or frames on the way in which the members of the frame are connected.

Steel is the material that is used in the majority of framed structures, either by itself or in combination with concrete because of its good compressive and tensile strength and favourable strength to weight ratio. The continuous process of hot rolling steel and cold forming steel strip produces a range of sections suited to the fabrication of economical structural frames. Steel has to be painted, coated or encased to inhibit corrosion that would otherwise gradually reduce the strength of the material.

Concrete has good compressive strength and poor tensile strength. It is used as reinforced concrete in structural frames for the benefit of the combination of the tensile strength of steel and the compressive strength of concrete and the protection against corrosion and damage by fire that the concrete gives to the steel reinforcement cast into it.

The stability of structural frames depends on the section and connections of the members used in the fabrication of lattice, portal, post and beam and space deck frames.

LATTICE TRUSS CONSTRUCTION

Symmetrical pitch truss construction

To this day the cheapest form of structure for single-storey, single-bay buildings is a frame of lattice steel trusses on columns covered with profiled steel or corrugated asbestos cement sheets. This structural frame and its covering provides basic shelter for storage and agricultural purposes. A single-bay symmetrical-pitch frame of lattice steel trusses supported on steel columns is illustrated in Fig. 2. The lattice steel trusses are fabricated from small, mild steel sections bolted, riveted or welded together to form a triangular symmetrical-pitch roof frame. The considerable depth of the roof frames at mid span provides adequate strength and rigidity in supporting dead and imposed roof loads. For maximum structural efficiency the slope or pitch of the truss should be not less than about 17 degrees to horizontal.

Steel columns support the roof trusses that are spaced at from 3.0 to 5.0 apart with steel purlins fixed across the trusses to support roof sheeting and steel sheeting rails fixed to the columns to support wall sheeting. The bolted, fixed base connection of the foot of the columns to the concrete foundation bases provides sufficient strength and stability against wind pressure on the side walls and roof, and wind bracing (see Fig. 17) provides stability against wind pressure on the end walls and gable end of the roof.

The advantage of this simple, single-storey, single-bay frame is economy in material by the use of small angle,

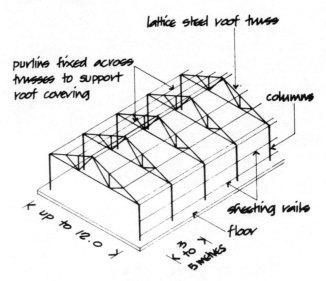

Single bay symmetrical pitch lattice steel roof on steel columns

Fig. 2

tube or flat standard mild steel sections for the roof trusses that can economically be fabricated and quickly erected on comparatively slender mild steel I-section columns fixed to concrete pad foundations.

The disadvantages of the frame are the very considerable volume of roof space inside the triangular roof frames which cannot be used for any purpose other than housing services such as lighting and heating. Where the activity enclosed by the building requires heating, the roof space has to be heated as well as the useful space below and the steel sections of the roof frames will collect dust and require frequent painting to inhibit rust.

For natural lighting a part of the roof may be covered with glass or profiled clear or translucent plastic sheets which are fixed in the slopes of the roof, usually in the middle third of each slope of the roof as illustrated in Fig. 3, to provide a reasonable penetration of light to the working surface in the building.

The thin sheets of profiled steel sheet or asbestos cement sheet that are used to provide cover to the walls of these buildings have poor resistance to damage by knocks. As an alternative to steel columns to support the roof trusses, brick side walls may be used for single-bay buildings to provide support for the roof frames, protection against wind and rain and solid resistance to damage by knocks. Fig. 4 is an illustration of a single-bay, single-storey building with brick side walls supporting steel roof trusses. The side walls are stiffened by piers built into them under the roof trusses.

The most economical span for symmetrical-pitch roof trusses is up to about 12.0 and the most economical spacing of trusses and columns, for economy in purlin and sheeting rail section, is from 3.0 to 5.0.

LATTICE TRUSS, BEAM, PORTAL FRAME AND FLAT ROOF CONSTRUCTION

North light steel lattice truss construction

Rooflights in the slope of symmetrical pitch roofs may cause discomfort through overheating in summer and disrupt manufacturing activities by the glare from sunlight.

To avoid these possibilities the north light roof is used. The north light roof has an asymmetrical pitch or slopes with the south facing slope at 17 degrees or more to horizontal and the north facing slope at from 60 degrees to horizontal. Fig. 5 is an illustration of a single-bay, single-storey building with north light lattice steel roof trusses on columns. The whole of the south slope is covered with profiled steel sheets or asbestos cement sheets and the whole of the north facing slope with glass or clear or translucent plastic sheeting as illustrated in Fig. 6.

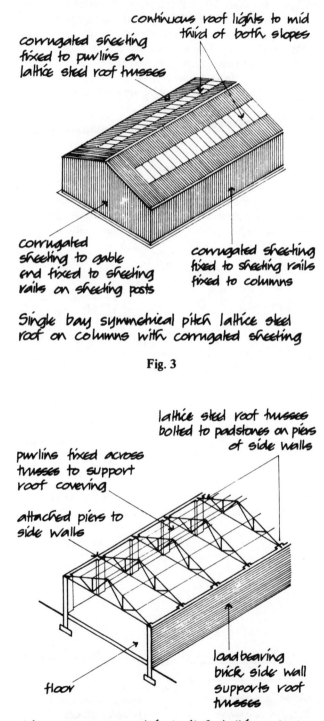

Single bay symmetrical pitch lattice steel roof on columns with corrugated sheeting

Fig. 3

Single bay symmetrical pitch lattice steel roof on brick side walls

Fig. 4

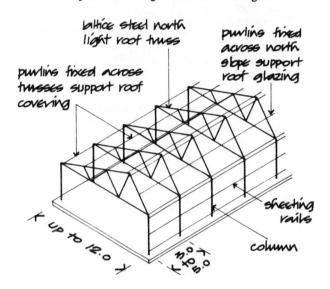

Single bay north light lattice steel roof trusses on steel columns

Fig. 5

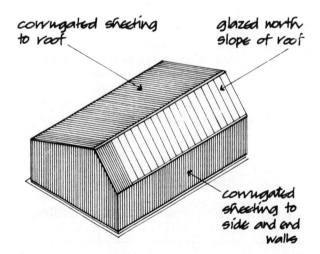

Single bay lattice steel north light roof on columns with corrugated sheeting

Fig. 6

Because of the steeply pitched slope of the north facing roof the space inside the roof trusses of a north light roof is considerably greater than that of a symmetrical pitch roof of the same span as illustrated in Fig. 7. To limit the volume of roof space that cannot be used and has to be wastefully heated, most north light truss roofs are limited to spans of up to about 10.0.

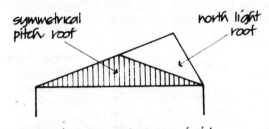

Comparison of roof space inside symmetrical pitch and north light roofs of the same span

Fig. 7

Multi-bay lattice steel roof truss construction

There is no theoretical limit to the span of a single-bay lattice steel roof truss to provide clear unobstructed floor area. For structural economy a triangular truss should have a pitch of not less than 17 degrees to the horizontal. With increase in span there is an increase in the volume of the unused space inside the roof trusses and length of the truss members. To cover large areas it is, therefore, usual to use two or more bays of symmetrical pitch roofs to limit the volume of roof space and length of members of the trusses. Fig. 8 is an illustration of the comparative volume of a single long-span roof and four smaller roof bays covering the same floor width.

To avoid the use of closely spaced internal columns to support roof trusses it is usual with multi-bay roofs to use either valley beams or lattice girders inside the depth of the trusses to reduce the number of internal columns that would otherwise obstruct the working floor area.

Multi-bay valley beam lattice steel truss roof

A beam under the valley of the roof supports the ends of roof trusses between the internal columns that support the valley beam, as illustrated in Fig. 9. Plainly the greater the span between internal columns supporting a valley beam the greater will be the depth of the valley beam, so that for a given required clear working height, an increase in the depth of the valley beam will increase the volume of unused roof space above the underside or soffit of the valley beam, as illustrated in Fig. 10.

Similarly a valley beam may be used in multi-bay north light truss roofs as illustrated in Fig. 11.

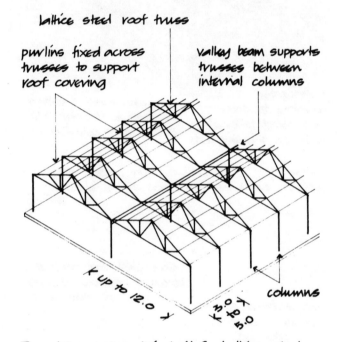

Two bay symmetrical pitch lattice steel roof and columns with valley beam

Fig. 9

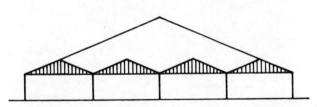

Comparison of volume of roof space and area of truss of one single and four trusses

Fig. 8

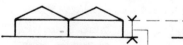

closely spaced internal columns

clear headroom

valley beam with widely spaced internal columns

Fig. 10

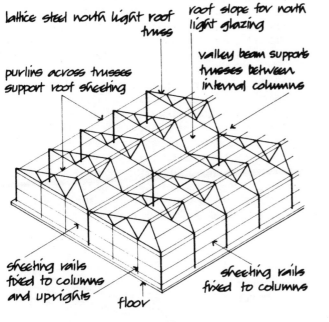

lattice steel north light roof truss

roof slope for north light glazing

purlins across trusses support roof sheeting

valley beam supports trusses between internal columns

sheeting rails fixed to columns and uprights

floor

sheeting rails fixed to columns

Two bay north light lattice steel roof with columns and valley beam

Fig. 11

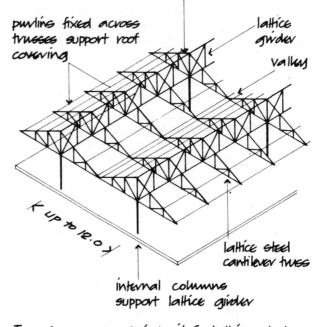

roof trusses cantilever each side of lattice girder

purlins fixed across trusses support roof covering

lattice girder

valley

K up to 12.0 J

lattice steel cantilever truss

internal columns support lattice girder

Two bay symmetrical pitch lattice steel cantilever (Umbrella) roof

Fig. 12

Cantilever (umbrella) multi-bay lattice steel roof construction

A lattice girder constructed inside the depth of each bay of symmetrical pitch roof trusses will, because of its great depth, be capable of supporting the roof between comparatively widely spaced internal columns and will not project below the underside of the trusses. Fig. 12 is an illustration of a cantilever or umbrella roof with lattice steel girders constructed inside the depth of each bay of trusses at mid span of bays. The lattice girder supports half of each truss with each half cantilevered each side of the truss, hence the name cantilever. The outline in section of the column and the truss cantilevered each side of the lattice girder, resembles an umbrella, hence the name umbrella roof.

North light multi-bay lattice steel roof construction

North light trusses may be supported by a lattice girder, as illustrated in Fig. 13, with widely spaced internal columns to cover large areas with the least obstruction. The profile of a multi-bay north light roof resembles the teeth of a saw, hence the name 'saw-tooth roof' that is often used for this type of roof.

The disadvantage of the cantilever roof form is the great number of lattice members in the roof of both the trusses and the lattice girders as these will collect dust and dirt, need frequent painting to inhibit rust and will to some extent obstruct natural light from rooflights.

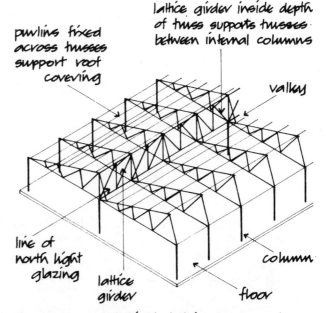

lattice girder inside depth of truss supports trusses between internal columns

purlins fixed across trusses support roof covering

valley

line of north light glazing

lattice girder

column

floor

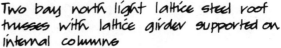

Two bay north light lattice steel roof trusses with lattice girder supported on internal columns

Fig. 13

Lattice steel truss construction

For the sake of the economy in using one standard section, lattice steel trusses are often fabricated from one standard mild steel angle section with two angles, back to back for the rafters and main tie, and a single angle for the internal struts and ties as illustrated in Fig. 14.

A common method of joining the members of a steel truss is by the use of steel gusset plates that are cut to shape to contain the required number of bolts or rivets at each connection. The flat steel gusset plates are fixed between the two angle sections of the rafters and main tie and to the intermediate ties and struts, as illustrated in Fig. 14. Bearing plates fixed to the foot of each truss provide a fixing to the cap plates of columns (Fig. 14).

The members of trusses may be bolted or riveted together through gusset plates. Whichever fastener is used will depend on economy in fabrication, transport and erection. Small numbers of small span trusses will have bolted connections and large numbers of medium span trusses riveted connections except for bolted connections at mid span, for the sake of ease of transporting half trusses to site and bolting them together on site ready for erection.

Standard I-section steel columns are used to support the roof trusses. A steel base plate is welded or fixed with bolted or riveted connections with gusset plates and angle cleats to the base of the columns. The column base plate is levelled on a grout of cement on the concrete pad foundation to which it is rigidly fixed with four holding down bolts cast or set into the foundation as illustrated in Fig. 15. The rigid fixing of the columns to the foundation bases provides stability to the column in resisting lateral wind pressure on the side walls of the building.

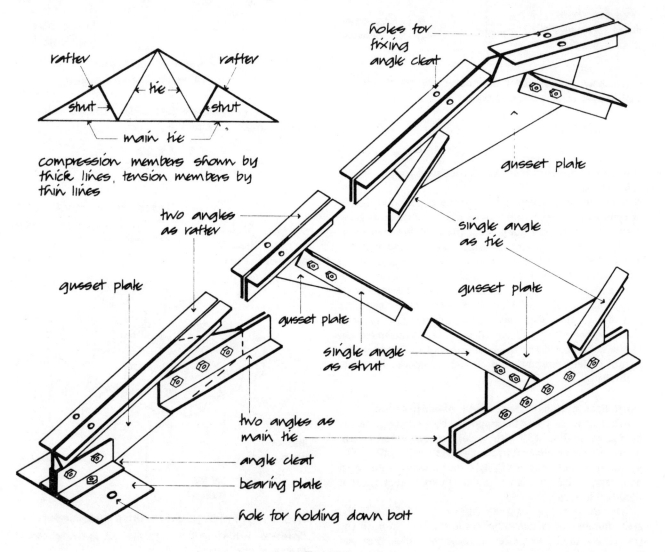

Fig. 14

LATTICE TRUSS, BEAM, PORTAL FRAME AND FLAT ROOF CONSTRUCTION

A cap is welded or fixed with bolted or riveted connections to the top of each column and the bearing plates of truss ends are bolted to the cap plates as illustrated in Fig. 15.

Lattice trusses can be fabricated from tubular steel sections that are cut, mitred and welded together as illustrated in Fig. 16. Because of the labour involved in cutting and welding the members, a tubular steel section truss is more expensive than an angle section truss. From the economy of fabricating standard trusses and the economy of repetition in producing many similar trusses a tubular steel section truss may be only a little more expensive than a similar one-off angle section truss.

The advantages of the tubular section truss are the greater structural efficiency of the tubular section over the angle section and the comparatively clean line of the tubulars and their welded connections which reduces the surface area liable to collect dust and needing to be painted.

The truss illustrated in Fig. 16 has a raised tie, the middle third of the length of the main tie being raised above the level of the foot of the truss. This raised tie affords some increase in working height below the raised part of the tie which plainly is only of advantage with medium- and long-span trusses.

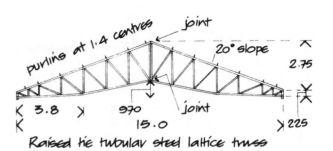

Raised tie tubular steel lattice truss

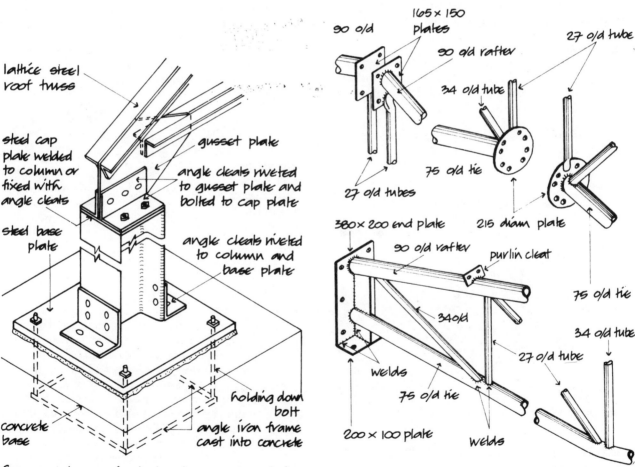

Cap and base of steel column support for lattice steel truss

Raised tie tubular steel lattice truss

Fig. 15

Fig. 16

Wind bracing to lattice truss frame buildings

The considerable depth at mid span and the lattice of members of roof trusses provides adequate rigidity and strength to support dead and imposed loads on the roof. The rigid connection of columns to foundations provides strength and rigidity in resisting horizontal loads from wind pressure on the side walls of the building.

The gable end walls of lattice truss frame buildings are stiffened against horizontal wind loads by gable wind girders fixed at the main tie level to form a lattice girder to transfer loads from the gable end to the sides of the structure, as illustrated in Fig. 17. Vertical wind bracing to both the side walls and the gable ends are fixed to provide additional stiffness against horizontal wind pressure on the gable end and side walls as illustrated in Fig. 17.

The rafter bracing illustrated in Fig. 17, which is fixed between adjacent trusses at the ends of the building, is used to square the frames during erection and to provide additional stiffness against horizontal wind pressure. The wall bracing is used to square the building during erection as well as stiffening against wind pressure.

Purlins and sheeting rails

Purlins are fixed across roof trusses and sheeting rails across columns to provide support and fixing for roof and wall sheeting and insulation. The spacing of purlins and sheeting rails depends on the roof and wall covering used. The deeper the profile of sheeting the greater its safe span hence the further apart purlins and sheeting rails can be fixed.

The section of purlins and sheeting rails depends on the most economic spacing of the trusses and columns to which they are fixed. The greater the spacing the greater the dead weight of sheeting and imposed loads, hence the deeper the section of purlin and sheeting rail needed to support the dead weight of the roof and wall covering and imposed loads from wind and snow.

Before 1960 most purlins and sheeting rails were of standard mild steel sections, angle section being common for most truss and column spacing and channel section for widely spaced structural frames.

Angle section purlins are fixed to short lengths of steel angle cleat welded, bolted or riveted to the top flanges of the rafters of roof trusses. Fig. 18 illustrates the bolted fixing of steel angle purlins to cleats with a short length of cleat for fixing along the length of a purlin and a longer cleat to make connection and provide a fixing at butt ends of purlin connections.

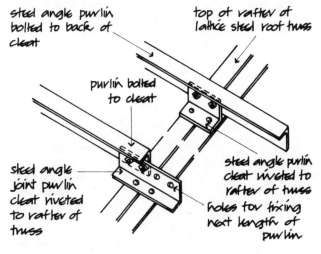

Connection of purlin to truss

Fig. 18

Similarly angle section sheeting rails are bolted to cleats welded, bolted or riveted to steel columns for the support and fixing of sheeting and insulation.

Gable end wall sheeting is supported by and fixed to sheeting rails that are in turn fixed to steel gable posts of tee, channel or I-section, bolted to a concrete pad foundation, an upstand kerb or the concrete floor and fixed to the gable end truss or portal roof frame as illustrated in Fig. 19. The gable end posts are fixed at centres to suit angle sheeting rails and gable wall sheeting.

Standard mild steel angles are not the most economical section for use as purlins and sheeting rails as the section is often considerably thicker than that required to support the dead weight and imposed loads of the roof and wall covering and the thickness of the standard angle is too great for the use of self-drilling fastenings.

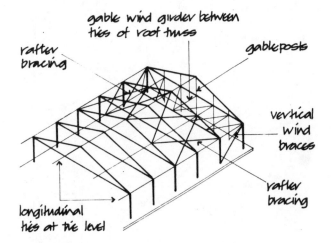

Wind bracing to lattice steel roof on steel columns.

Fig. 17

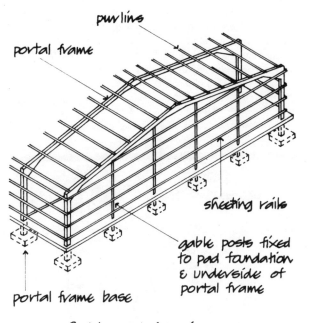

purlins

portal frame

sheeting rails

gable posts fixed to pad foundation & underside of portal frame

portal frame base

Gable end framing

Fig. 19

Since about 1960 a range of cold formed steel strip purlins and sheeting rails has been produced and designed specifically for the purpose. The two sections in common use are the zed section for general use and the multi-beam section for more widely spaced trusses and portal frames. Fig. 20 is an illustration of the sections of mild steel angle, zed and multi-beam used for purlins and sheeting rails. The thin section of the zed and multi-beam purlins and sheeting rails facilitates the use of self-drilling self-tapping fasteners that can be driven, with a power operated tool, through steel sheeting and the purlin in one operation.

Zed and multi-beam purlins and sheeting rails are bolted to steel angle cleats welded, bolted or riveted to the top of trusses or frames and to columns and gable posts.

Because of their comparatively slender section, zed and multi-beam purlins of over 4.5 span between supports tend to sag or bow while the sheeting is being fixed or due to wind uplift on the roof covering. To prevent this sag, a system of sag rods is fixed at mid span of purlins, as illustrated in Fig. 21. For their economy in section and the facility of fixing fasteners, zed sections are used for fixing and supporting most profiled steel roof and wall sheeting today.

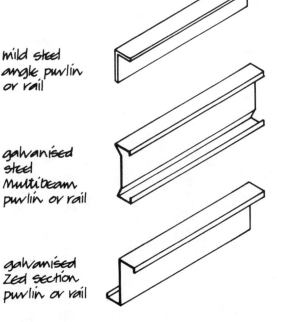

mild steel angle purlin or rail

galvanised steel Multibeam purlin or rail

galvanised Zed section purlin or rail

Steel section purlin and sheeting rails to support sheet metal and asbestos cement sheeting

Fig. 20

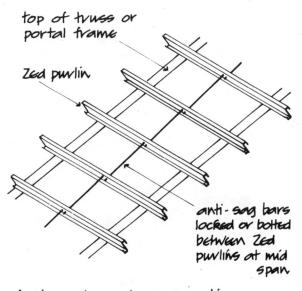

top of truss or portal frame

Zed purlin

anti-sag bars locked or bolted between Zed purlins at mid span

Anti-sag bars to Zed purlins

Fig. 21

LATTICE BEAM ROOF CONSTRUCTION

The advantage of the lattice truss roof is the strength and rigidity provided by the considerable depth of the trusses at mid span. With increase in span the depth of a truss at mid span and the volume of unused roof space increases to the extent that it is generally economical to use another roof form for medium- and long-span roofs. A lattice beam roof is less structurally efficient in the use of material than a lattice truss roof of similar span but can be constructed as a sloping or low pitch roof to minimise the volume of unused roof space.

A lattice beam roof consists of cranked lattice beams spanning between columns as shown in Fig. 22 which illustrates a single-bay, single-storey, symmetrical-pitch lattice beam roof. The lattice beams are fabricated from standard mild steel angle sections or more usually from tubular steel sections that are cut, mitred and welded together with bolted site connections at mid span to facilitate the transportation of half beam sections. End plates welded to the lattice beams are bolted to the flanges of I-section steel columns.

The pitch or slope of lattice beam roofs is usually from 5 to 10 degrees to the horizontal and zed or multi-beam purlins, fixed across the beams, support profiled steel sheeting or metal decking.

Multi-bay lattice beam roofs are constructed with lattice girder valley beams supporting lattice roof beams between widely spaced internal columns to provide least obstruction to floor space.

A two-bay lattice beam roof frame is illustrated in Fig. 23. This roof is sometimes described as a 'butterfly' roof because of its outline.

The 'saw tooth' two-bay north light lattice beam roof illustrated in Fig. 24 is constructed with lattice beams fixed to the top and bottom booms of an internal lattice girder that is supported by widely spaced internal columns with the lattice beams supported by steel columns externally. The lattice beam acts as a frame for the north facing glazing that may either be fixed to vertical glazing bars or fixed in the triangles of the lattice.

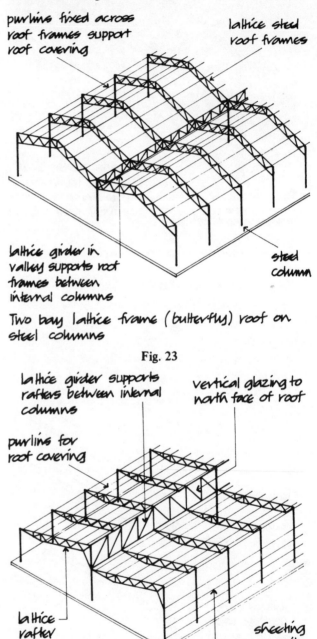

purlins fixed across roof frames support roof covering

lattice steel roof frames

lattice girder in valley supports roof frames between internal columns

steel column

Two bay lattice frame (butterfly) roof on steel columns

Fig. 23

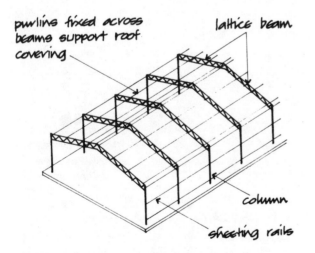

purlins fixed across beams support roof covering

lattice beam

column

sheeting rails

Single bay symmetrical pitch lattice beam and column frame

Fig. 22

lattice girder supports rafters between internal columns

vertical glazing to north face of roof

purlins for roof covering

lattice rafter

sheeting rails

Two bay lattice rafter sawtooth roof with lattice girder supported on internal columns

Fig. 24

PORTAL FRAMES

Following the acceptance of the plastic theory of design, proposed by Professor Baker, rigid steel portal frames became an economic alternative to lattice truss and lattice beam roofs.

The application of the plastic theory in place of the previous generally used elastic method of design (see Volume 4) is particularly relevant to rigid frames of a ductile material such as steel. The plastic theory takes account of the distribution of moments through the whole of the rigid frame under working loads so that sections lighter and more slender than sections determined by the elastic method of design may be used safely.

For structural efficiency a pitched roof portal frame should have as low a pitch as practical to minimise spread at the knees of the portal frame (spread increases with the pitch of the roof of a portal frame). The knee of a portal frame is the rigid connection of the rafter to the post of the portal.

The early use of the rigid portal frame coincided with the introduction of a wide range of cold formed profiled steel sheets for roofing, which could be fixed at a low pitch and be weathertight. The combination of low pitch steel portal frames and profiled steel roof sheeting and decking has led to the adoption of this form of structure for the majority of single-storey structures today.

Steel portal frames

A portal frame is distinguished by the rigid connection of the rafters to the posts of the frame so that under load moments are distributed through the rafter and the post. For short- and medium-span portal frames the apex or ridge, where the rafters connect, is generally made as an on-site rigid bolted connection for convenience in transporting half portal frames. Long-span portal frames may have a pin joint connection at the ridge to allow some flexure between the rafters of the frame which are pin jointed to foundation bases.

For economy in the use of a standard section, short- and medium-span steel portal frames are often fabricated from one mild steel I section for both rafters and posts, with the rafters welded to the posts without any increase in depth at the knee as illustrated in Fig. 25.

Short-span portal frames may be fabricated off site as one frame. Medium-span portal frames are generally fabricated in two halves for ease of transport and assembled on site with bolted connections of the rafters at the ridge, with high strength friction grip (hsfg) bolts (see Volume 4).

Many medium- and long-span steel portal frames have the connection of the rafters to the posts, at the knee, haunched to make the connection deeper than the main rafter section for additional stiffness as illustrated in Fig. 26. In long-span steel portal frames the posts may often be fabricated from cut and welded I sections so that the post section is wider at the knee or connection to the rafter than at the base (Fig. 27).

The haunched connection of the rafter to the posts can be fabricated either by welding a cut I section to the underside of the rafter, as illustrated in Fig. 26, or by cutting and bending the bottom flange of the rafter and welding in a steel gusset plate.

The junction of rafters at the apex is often stiffened by welding cut I sections to the underside of the rafters at the bolted site connection at the apex as shown in Fig. 28.

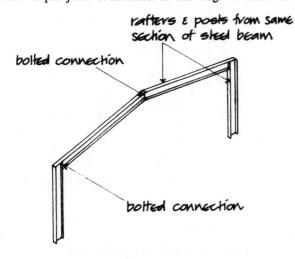

Short span steel portal frame

Fig. 25

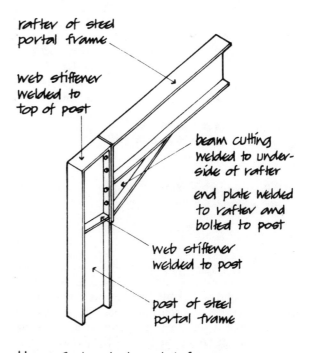

Haunch to steel portal frame

Fig. 26

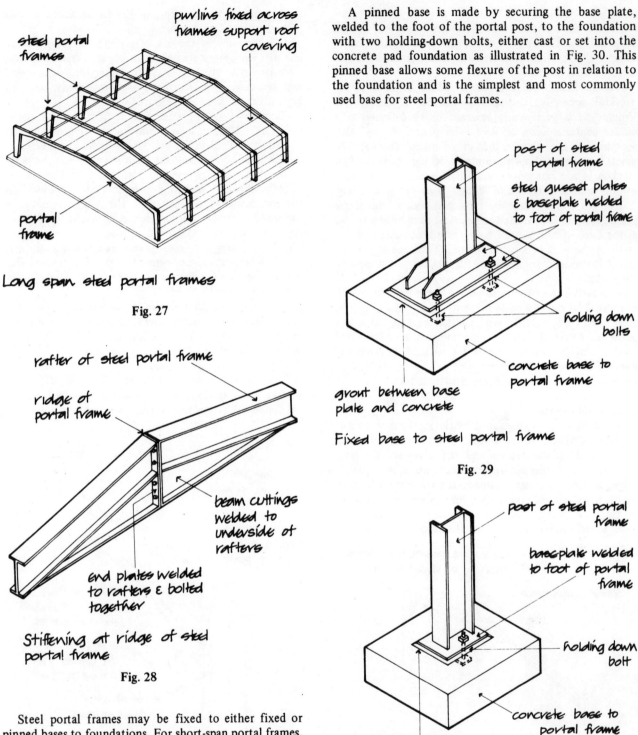

steel portal frames

purlins fixed across frames support roof covering

portal frame

Long span steel portal frames

Fig. 27

rafter of steel portal frame

ridge of portal frame

beam cuttings welded to underside of rafters

end plates welded to rafters & bolted together

Stiffening at ridge of steel portal frame

Fig. 28

A pinned base is made by securing the base plate, welded to the foot of the portal post, to the foundation with two holding-down bolts, either cast or set into the concrete pad foundation as illustrated in Fig. 30. This pinned base allows some flexure of the post in relation to the foundation and is the simplest and most commonly used base for steel portal frames.

post of steel portal frame

steel gusset plates & baseplate welded to foot of portal frame

holding down bolts

concrete base to portal frame

grout between base plate and concrete

Fixed base to steel portal frame

Fig. 29

Steel portal frames may be fixed to either fixed or pinned bases to foundations. For short-span portal frames, where there is comparatively little spread at the knee or haunch, a fixed base is sometimes used. It will be seen from Fig. 29 that the steel base plate, which is welded through gusset plates to the post of the portal frame, is set level on a bed of cement grout on the concrete pad foundation and is secured by four holding-down bolts set or cast into the concrete foundation.

post of steel portal frame

baseplate welded to foot of portal frame

holding down bolt

concrete base to portal frame

grout between base plate and concrete

Pinned base to steel portal frame

Fig. 30

14

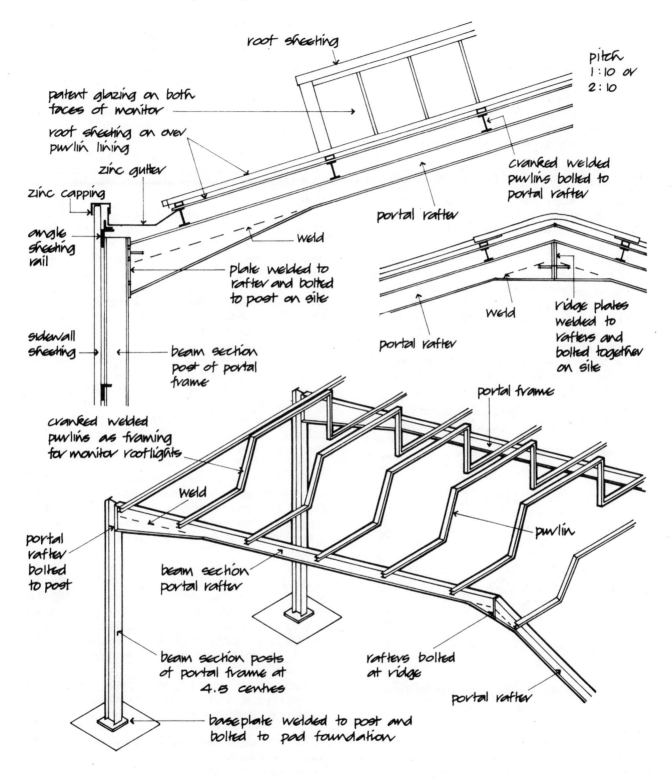

roof sheeting

pitch
1:10 or
2:10

patent glazing on both
faces of monitor

roof sheeting on over
purlin lining

zinc gutter

zinc capping

angle
sheeting
rail

sidewall
sheeting

cranked welded
purlins bolted to
portal rafter

portal rafter

weld

plate welded to
rafter and bolted
to post on site

beam section
post of portal
frame

weld

portal rafter

ridge plates
welded to
rafters and
bolted together
on site

portal frame

cranked welded
purlins as framing
for monitor rooflights

weld

portal
rafter
bolted
to post

beam section
portal rafter

beam section posts
of portal frame at
4.5 centres

baseplate welded to post and
bolted to pad foundation

purlin

rafters bolted
at ridge

portal rafter

Solid web steel portal frame with monitor roof lights

Fig. 31

Short-span portal frames are usually spaced at from 3.0 to 5.0 apart and medium-span portal frames at from 4.0 to 8.0 apart to suit the use of angle or cold-formed purlins illustrated in Fig. 20. Long-span steel portal frames are usually spaced at from 8.0 to 12.0 apart to economise in the number of the comparatively expensive frames, with channels, I-section or lattice purlins and sheeting rails to support roof sheeting or decking and wall sheeting.

With flat or sloping steel portal frames it is not possible to ensure a watertight system of roof glazing, fixed in the slope of the roof covering, with either glass or profiled plastic sheets. For natural roof lighting a system of monitor roof lights is often used. These lights are formed by welded, cranked I-section steel purlins fixed across the portal frames as illustrated in Fig. 31. The monitor lights project above the roof level with two upstand faces that may be vertical or sloping. The monitor lights shown in Fig. 31 are designed with the vertical face facing south to minimise the penetration of direct sunlight and the sloping face facing north to provide a good distribution of natural light to the interior. The monitor lights can be constructed to provide natural or controlled ventilation. Fig. 32 is an illustration of a single-bay portal frame building with monitor lights. It will be seen that the monitor lights finish short of the eaves to avoid the difficulty of finish at eaves that would otherwise occur.

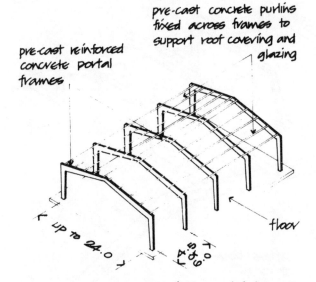

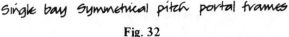

Single bay symmetrical pitch portal frames

Fig. 32

Pre-cast concrete portal frames

In the years immediately following the end of the Second World War there was a considerable shortage of structural steel in this country and it was then that concrete portal frames came into common use for agricultural, storage, factory and other single-storey buildings.

The manufacturers of pre-cast reinforced concrete portal frames supply a range of standard frames for the benefit of repetitive casting in standard moulds and the benefit of close control of the mixing, placing and compacting of concrete that is possible in factory conditions. These standard concrete frames are economic in first cost for short- and medium-span single-storey buildings. Departure from the standard frames greatly increases the cost of a pre-cast reinforced concrete portal frame.

The advantages of reinforced concrete portal frames are that they require no maintenance during the useful life of a building and the frame has a somewhat better resistance to collapse during fires than an unprotected steel frame.

Because of the non-ductile nature of the principal material of these frames, concrete, the advantage of economy of section area gained by the use of the plastic method in the design of steel frames is considerably less with reinforced concrete frames. Because of the necessary section area of concrete and the cover of concrete to the steel reinforcement to inhibit rust and give protection to the steel reinforcement against damage during fires, the sections of concrete frames are large compared to steel frames of similar span. Damage to the frame and shrinkage cracks may rapidly cause rusting of the reinforcement particularly in wet and humid conditions.

For convenience in casting, transport and erection on site, pre-cast concrete portal frames are generally cast in two or more sections which are bolted together on site either at the point of contraflexure in rafters or at the junction of post and rafter, or both, as illustrated in Fig. 33.

The point of contraflexure is that position along the rafters where negative or upward bending changes to positive or downward bending. At this point the member is presumed to be suffering no bending stresses so that structurally this is the soundest point to make a connection.

Concrete portal frames are usually spaced at from 4.5 to 6.0 apart to support pre-cast reinforced concrete purlins cast in lengths to span between frames and bolted to the rafters. As an alternative cold-formed steel zed purlins may be used for the facility of fixing profiled steel sheeting. Similarly either pre-cast reinforced concrete, or steel zed section sheeting rails are fixed to the posts for side wall sheeting.

The bases of concrete portal frames are placed in mortices cast in concrete pad or strip foundations and the posts are grouted in position.

Symmetrical-pitch reinforced concrete portal frames: This is the most structurally efficient and most commonly used shape of concrete portal frame. It is used for factories, warehouses, barns, sheds and single-storey places of assembly. Fig. 32 is an illustration of a single-bay symmetrical-pitch pre-cast reinforced concrete portal frame.

The slope of the rafters and spacing of purlins is usually arranged to suit asbestos cement or profiled steel sheeting.

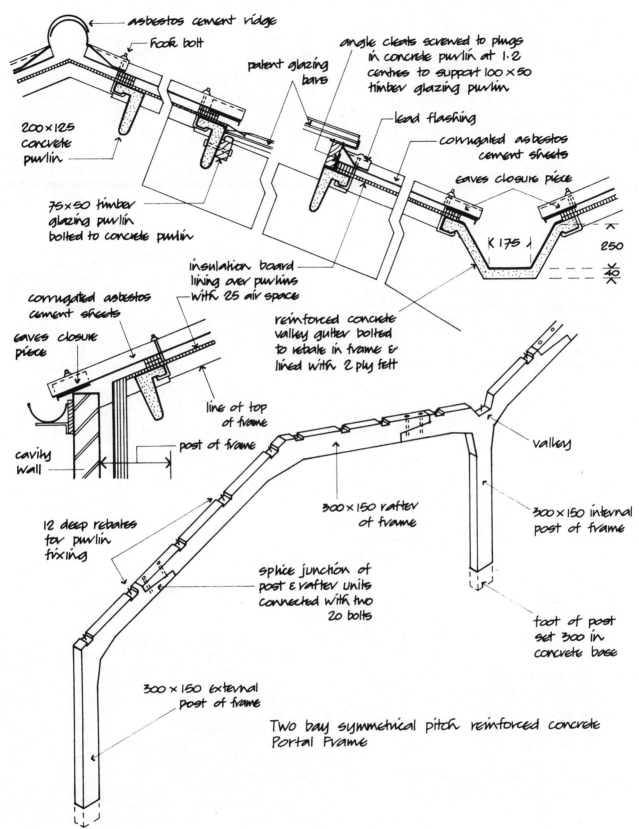

asbestos cement ridge

hook bolt

patent glazing bars

angle cleats screwed to plugs in concrete purlin at 1·2 centres to support 100 × 50 timber glazing purlin

lead flashing

200 × 125 concrete purlin

corrugated asbestos cement sheets

eaves closure piece

75 × 50 timber glazing purlin bolted to concrete purlin

175

250

40

insulation board lining over purlins with 25 air space

reinforced concrete valley gutter bolted to rebate in frame & lined with 2 ply felt

corrugated asbestos cement sheets

eaves closure piece

line of top of frame

post of frame

cavity wall

12 deep rebates for purlin fixing

300 × 150 rafter of frame

valley

300 × 150 internal post of frame

splice junction of post & rafter units connected with two 20 bolts

foot of post set 300 in concrete base

300 × 150 external post of frame

Two bay symmetrical pitch reinforced concrete Portal Frame

Fig. 33

17

Fig. 33 is an illustration of the details of a two-bay symmetrical-pitch concrete portal frame. It will be seen that the rafter, which is cast as one unit, is bolted to the posts at the point of contraflexure as previously described. A single post supports the rafters of the frames below the valley in the roof and these posts are shaped to receive a pre-cast reinforced concrete valley gutter bolted to the rafters which is laid without fall to rainwater pipes and is lined with felt. The spacing of internal columns below valleys may be increased by the use of a pre-cast or in-situ-cast cement-and-sand mortar, as illustrated in Fig. 34 practice is to utilise a valley beam spanning about 9.0 or 14.0 to support intermediate rafter ends.

The pre-cast reinforced concrete purlins are usually of angle section with stiffening ribs and cast in lengths to span between portal rafters. The purlins are fixed by loops protruding from their ends, which fit over and are bolted to studs cast in the rafters, and the joint is completed with situ-cast cement- and sand-mortar, as illustrated in Fig. 34.

Corrugated asbestos cement sheeting is hook bolted to the concrete purlins over an insulating lining laid over the purlins as illustrated in Fig. 33. As an alternative, profiled steel sheeting with an insulating lining may be fixed to zed purlins bolted to the rafters of the portal frames.

Walls may be of solid brick or concrete block fixed between or across the posts of the portal frames, or asbestos cement or profiled steel sheeting can be used.

North light pre-cast reinforced concrete portal frames: The most economical span for this profile of frame is up to about 9.0 to minimise the volume of roof space inside the frames and to avoid the large sections of frame that would be necessary with greater spans.

The south facing slope is pitched at 22½ degrees and the north facing slope at from 60 to 90 degrees to the horizontal. Fig. 35 illustrates the frame of a typical two-bay north light concrete portal frame.

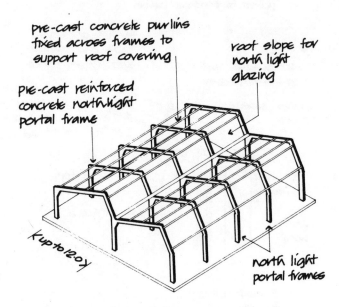

pre-cast concrete purlins fixed across frames to support roof covering

root slope for north light glazing

pre-cast reinforced concrete northlight portal frame

north light portal frames

Kup to 12.0

Two bay north light portal frames

Fig. 35

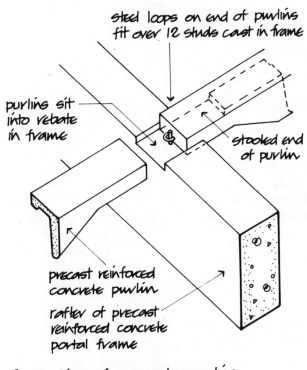

steel loops on end of purlins fit over 12 studs cast in frame

purlins sit into rebate in frame

stooled end of purlin

precast reinforced concrete purlin

rafter of precast reinforced concrete portal frame

Connection of concrete purlins to concrete portal frame

Fig. 34

From Fig. 36 it will be seen that for convenience in casting and transport the rafter is cast in two sections which are bolted together at the point of contraflexure and in turn bolted to the posts. A pre-cast reinforced concrete valley gutter is bolted to the frames as previously described.

Pre-cast reinforced concrete purlins or steel zed purlins are bolted to the rafters to support wood wool slabs, or asbestos cement or profiled steel sheets and north light glazing is fixed to timber purlins.

In the example illustrated in Fig. 36 a pre-cast reinforced concrete eaves beam serves as purlin and provides support for the eaves gutter. The spacing of internal posts of multi-span north light portals can be increased by the use of a concrete valley beam.

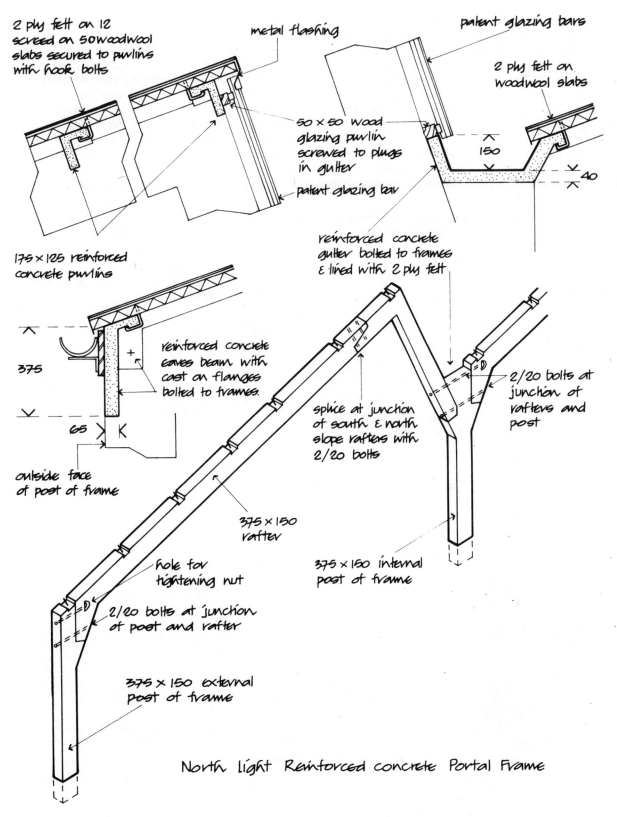

2 ply felt on 12 screed on 50 woodwool slabs secured to purlins with hook bolts

metal flashing

patent glazing bars

2 ply felt on woodwool slabs

50 × 50 wood glazing purlin screwed to plugs in gutter

patent glazing bar

150

40

reinforced concrete gutter bolted to frames & lined with 2 ply felt

175 × 125 reinforced concrete purlins

reinforced concrete eaves beam with cast on flanges bolted to frames.

375

65

outside face of post of frame

2/20 bolts at junction of rafters and post

splice at junction of south & north slope rafters with 2/20 bolts

375 × 150 rafter

hole for tightening nut

375 × 150 internal post of frame

2/20 bolts at junction of post and rafter

375 × 150 external post of frame

North Light Reinforced Concrete Portal Frame

Fig. 36

19

Timber portal frames

The limitation of natural timber as a structural material is its variable strength. Two similar members cut from a log may well have different resistances to tensile and compressive stress and this fact did for some time limit the economic use of timber. If, however, several slender timber sections are strongly glued together the resulting member is stronger than the weakest section from which it is fabricated.

Combinations of slender timber sections glued or glued and nailed together are used in portal frames for medium- and long-span roofs for churches, assembly halls, sports halls and other single-storey medium- and long-span buildings where the portal frames are exposed for their appearance sake.

The advantage of timber as a structural material in this form is its low self-weight and the comparatively little maintenance required to preserve and maintain the appearance of it. The resistance to damage and collapse of structural timber during a fire depends to a large extent on the sectional area of the timber which, when burned, first chars and the charred outer surface provides considerable protection from fire to the timber below.

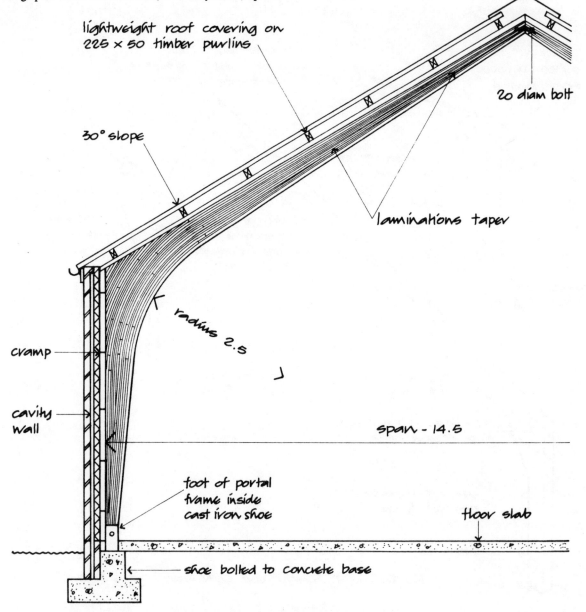

lightweight roof covering on 225 × 50 timber purlins

20 diam bolt

30° slope

laminations taper

radius 2.5

cramp

cavity wall

span - 14.5

foot of portal frame inside cast iron shoe

floor slab

shoe bolted to concrete base

Glued laminated timber portal frame

Fig. 37

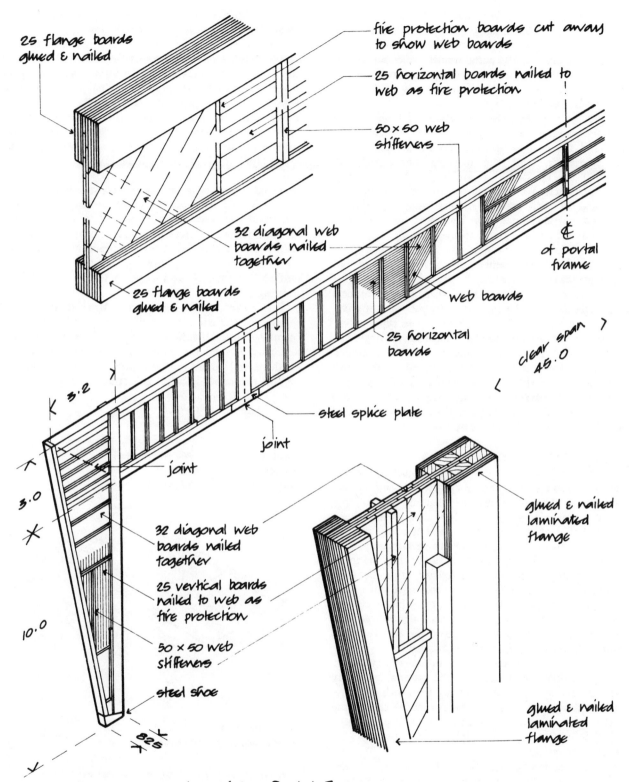

25 flange boards glued & nailed

fire protection boards cut away to show web boards

25 horizontal boards nailed to web as fire protection

50 × 50 web stiffeners

32 diagonal web boards nailed together

25 flange boards glued & nailed

web boards

25 horizontal boards

℄ of portal frame

clear span 45.0

3.2

3.0

10.0

825

steel splice plate

joint

joint

32 diagonal web boards nailed together

25 vertical boards nailed to web as fire protection

50 × 50 web stiffeners

steel shoe

glued & nailed laminated flange

glued & nailed laminated flange

Glued and nailed timber Portal Frame

Fig. 38

21

Symmetrical-pitch glued laminated timber portal: These portal roof frames are usually fabricated in two sections which are erected and bolted together at the ridge as illustrated in Fig. 37. The portal frames, which are expensive, are spaced fairly widely apart to support timber or steel purlins which can be covered with any of the sheet roofing materials or tiles or slates.

It will be seen that the laminations of timber, from which the portal is made, are arranged to taper in both the rafter and the post so that the depth is greatest at the knee, where the frame tends to spread under load, and slender at the apex or ridge and the foot of the post, where least section is required for strength and rigidity.

Because of their graceful arch-like appearance, glued laminated portal frames have been used for churches, community centres and places of assembly.

Flat glued-and-nailed timber portal: This type of flat timber portal is designed for the most economic use of timber and consists of a web of small section timbers glued together with the top and bottom booms of glued laminate with web stiffeners (Fig. 38). This type of flat, long-span portal has been used for single-storey, single-bay structures such as airplane hangars, with the comparatively expensive portals widely spaced and covered with metal decking on the roof and profiled steel sheeting to the walls. The advantage of this type of timber portal frame is the wide span, freedom from maintenance and reasonable resistance to damage by fire.

FLAT ROOF FRAME CONSTRUCTION

The design of buildings is often more subject to the dictates of fashion than economy in first cost, utility and maintenance. The appearance of single-storey buildings such as factories covering large floor areas, is influenced by the profile of the roof structure. For many years it has been fashionable to adopt the strong horizontal roof line or lines of a flat roof structure rather than the more economical single- or multi-bay pitched roof profile. Over the years these large areas of flat roofs have come into disrepute due to the flat roof coverings which have not remained watertight for long because of movements of the covering on the roof surface and the structure and failures at junctions to parapets and rooflights.

Recent improvements in flat roof bitumen felt weatherings, to improve the elasticity of the material and delay brittle hardening by oxidisation together with improvements in design detailing to allow for movements of the weather surface and roof support, have improved the useful life of flat roofs to compare favourably with profiled sheet coverings.

Medium- and long-span flat roof structures are less efficient structurally and therefore more expensive than portal frames. The main reason for this is the need to prevent too large a deflection of the flat roof structure under load to the accepted 1/250 of span and to limit deflection to prevent ponding of rainwater on flat roofs.

For these reasons flat roof beams or girders have to be deeper than is necessary for strength alone.

Ponding is the word used to describe the effect of rainwater lying in the centre of flat roofs, where deflection under load is greatest, in the form of a shallow pond of water that cannot drain to the outlets. A static pond of water will plainly penetrate faults in the roof covering more readily than water running off to gutters or outlets.

To avoid ponding either the roof surface has to have a positive fall under load to outlets or the structure must have a taper or fall to outlets under load.

Main and secondary beam flat roof construction

Fig. 39 is an illustration of a single-bay flat roof structure with solid web I-section main beams supported by steel columns and with I-section secondary beams between the main beams. Either the secondary beams are fixed across the roof to provide a positive slope to each side of the roof or a fall has to be formed in the base of the roof covering.

This heavy construction is not structurally efficient because of the considerable depth required in the main beams to limit deflection under load. This type of structure may be used for single-bay short- and medium-span buildings and where the main beams are used to provide support for travelling cranes and other lifting gear.

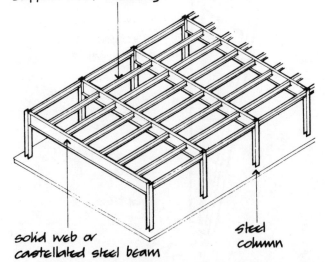

steel secondary beams fixed between main beams to support roof decking

solid web or castellated steel beam

steel column

Single bay flat roof with main and secondary beams on steel columns

Fig. 39

The main beams can be of castellated construction (see Volume 4) where the web of a standard beam is cut and welded together to form a beam with openings in the web to reduce the dead weight of the beam. A castellated main beam will, by its depth, have adequate stiffness to limit deflection under load and the perforations of the web can provide space for services.

Lattice girder flat roof construction

The required depth of beams for flat roof construction is determined by the need to limit deflection under load by the rigidity of depth more than the weight of material in the beam. A lattice girder of comparatively small section members fixed between the top and bottom boom of the beam at once provides adequate stiffness and economy in the use of material and low self-weight. Because lattice beams have to be fabricated it is an advantage to taper or pitch the top boom of the beams to provide a positive fall or slope under load to avoid ponding. A taper or low pitch lattice girder may be specially fabricated or one of the range of standard taper or low-pitch beams can be used.

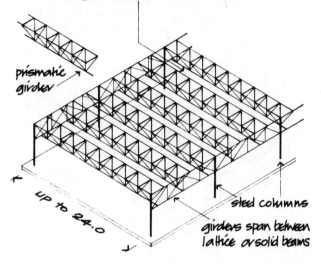

prismatic (V beam) lattice steel girders spaced up to 4.5 apart with decking or roof lights between beams

prismatic girder

up to 24.0

steel columns

girders span between lattice or solid beams

Prismatic (V beam) lattice steel roof on steel columns

Fig. 41

Fig. 40 is an illustration of typical standard taper and low-pitch lattice beams for flat roof construction. The beams are made from cold-formed steel strip 'top hat' sections for the top and bottom booms with a lattice of mild steel rods welded to the booms. The steel is finished with a stove-enamelled primer ready for painting. The top hat section of the booms is designed to take timber inserts for fixing roof and ceiling finishes. These standard lattice beams are considerably cheaper than one-off beams, through the economy of mass production.

V beam flat roof construction

A system of V section standard grid lattice beams is supported by end lattice beams supported on steel columns. The V section or prismatic beams are fabricated from tubular steel sections welded together. The V beams are spaced to support metal decking across the whole of the roof or the V beams can be spaced apart to suit continuous or separate rooflights. Fig. 41 is an illustration of a single-bay, single-storey lattice V beam structure. With standard section, standard span lattice V beams, a reasonably economic single- or multi-span flat roof structure can be built.

Space grid flat roof construction

A two-layer space deck constructed of a grid of standard units is one of the commonly used flat roof structures for single-storey buildings such as sports halls, shopping centres leisure halls and factories. Fig. 42 illustrates a single-storey structure with a space deck flat roof supported on steel columns.

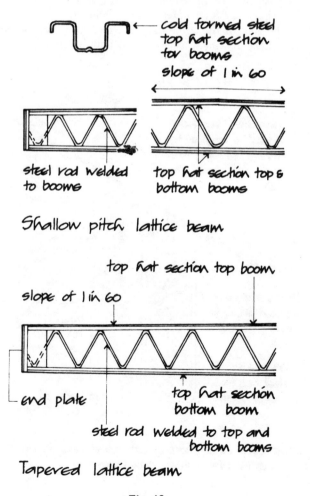

cold formed steel top hat section for booms

slope of 1 in 60

steel rod welded to booms

top hat section top & bottom booms

Shallow pitch lattice beam

top hat section top boom

slope of 1 in 60

end plate

top hat section bottom boom

steel rod welded to top and bottom booms

Tapered lattice beam

Fig. 40

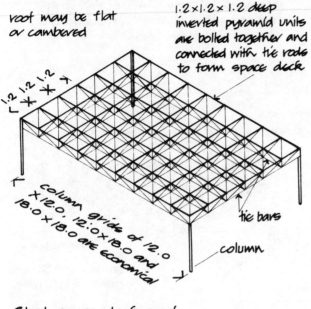

roof may be flat or cambered

1.2 × 1.2 × 1.2 deep inverted pyramid units are bolted together and connected with tie rods to form space deck

1.2 1.2 1.2

column grids of 12.0 × 12.0, 12.0 × 18.0 and 18.0 × 18.0 are economical

tie bars

column

Steel space deck roof

Fig. 42

The space deck is assembled on site from standard space deck units each in the form of an inverted pyramid with a steel angle tray base, tubular diagonals welded to the tray and a coupling boss as illustrated in Fig. 43. The space deck units are bolted together through the angle trays and connected with tie bars through the coupling bosses. The tie bars which have right- and left-hand threads can be adjusted to give an upward camber to the top of the deck to allow for deflection under load and to provide a positive fall to the roof to encourage run-off of rainwater and so avoid ponding.

Space deck roofs may be designed as either two-way spanning structures with a square column grid or as one-way spanning structures with a rectangular column grid. Economic column grids are 12.0 × 12.0, 18.0 × 18.0 and 12.0 × 18.0. Various arrangements of the column grid are feasible and also a variety of roof levels, canopies and overhangs.

The advantages of the space deck roof are the comparatively wide spacing of the supporting steel columns, economy of structure in the use of standard units and speed of erection. The disadvantage of the space deck is the great number of lattice members that will collect dust and require careful maintenance to inhibit rust.

The roof of the structural space deck may be covered with steel decking, insulation and built-up bitumen felt

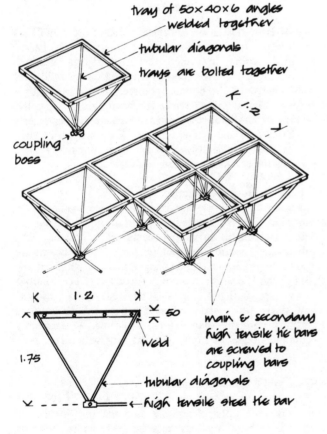

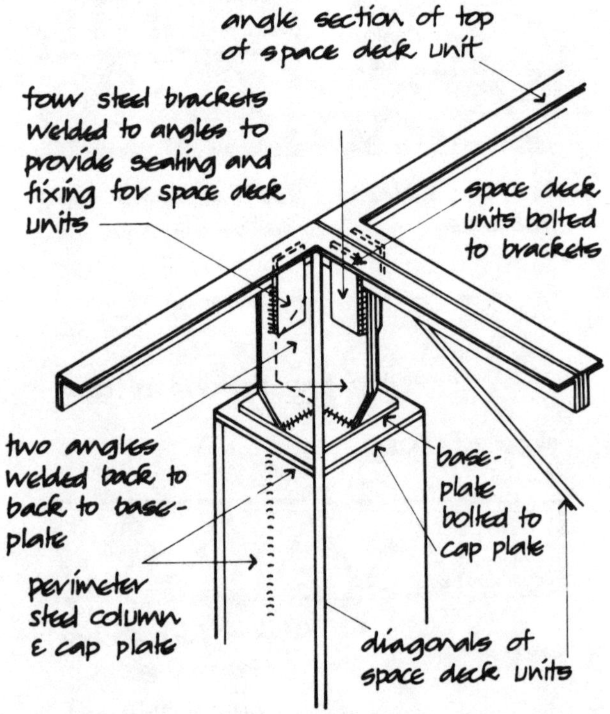

tray of 50×40×6 angles welded together

tubular diagonals

trays are bolted together

1.2

coupling boss

1.2

50

weld

1.75

main & secondary high tensile tie bars are screwed to coupling bars

tubular diagonals

high tensile steel tie bar

Steel space deck units

Fig. 43

angle section of top of space deck unit

four steel brackets welded to angles to provide seating and fixing for space deck units

space deck units bolted to brackets

two angles welded back to back to base-plate

base-plate bolted to cap plate

perimeter steel column & cap plate

diagonals of space deck units

Support and fixing of space deck units to perimeter steel columns

Fig. 44

roofing or wood wool slabs and bitument felt roofing, with rooflights made to suit the size of the standard units or units of the space deck.

Steel columns supporting the space deck are usually connected to the units at the junction of the trays of the units. Fig. 44 is an illustration of the junction of a column at the perimeter of the structure. It will be seen that a steel cap plate is welded to the head of the column to which a seating is bolted. This seating of steel angles has brackets welded to it into which the flanges of the trays fit and to which the trays are bolted. Likewise a seating is bolted to a cap plate of internal columns with brackets into which the flanges of the angles of four trays fit, as shown in Fig. 45.

The space deck can be finished with either flat or sloping eaves at perimeter columns or the deck can be cantilevered beyond the edge columns as an overhang. Fig. 46 shows a two-deck unit overhang and a fixed base with the column bolted to the concrete pad foundation.

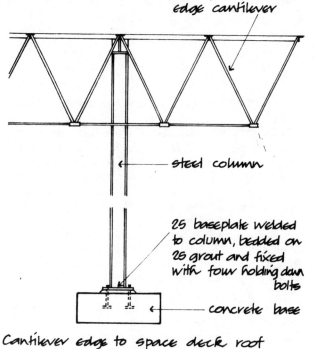

Cantilever edge to space deck roof

Fig. 46

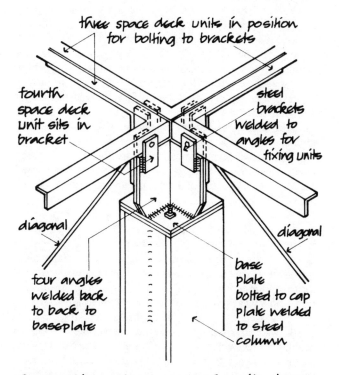

Connection of space deck units to an internal column.

Fig. 45

CHAPTER TWO

ROOF AND WALL SHEETING AND DECKING

PROFILED SHEET COVERINGS FOR ROOFS AND WALLS

Corrugated iron sheets were first produced about 1830 from wrought or puddled iron which was coated with zinc and either pressed or rolled to the corrugated profile. Because of the purity of the iron, the thickness of the sheets and the zinc coating, the original corrugated iron sheets had a useful life of more than fifty years in all but the most corrosive atmospheres.

After steel making became a commercial proposition in about 1860, thin corrugated steel sheets were first used in Britain about 1880. These thin corrugated steel sheets were considerably cheaper than the original iron sheets but had a useful life of only about a quarter that of the heavier iron sheet because the 'impurities' in the steel promoted more rapid corrosion even when the sheets were zinc coated. The comparatively rapid destructive corrosion of steel sheets led to the use of the non-corrosive alternative asbestos cement early in the twentieth century.

In the early days of the use of corrugated steel sheets it was common practice to protect the sheets against corrosion by coating them with tar, pitch or paint. So long as these coatings adhered strongly to the whole surface and edges of the sheets, corrosion did not occur. Once the coating was broken then rust spread rapidly between the steel and the coating and frequent chipping and wire brushing of the sheets was necessary followed by the application of protective coatings.

In 1883 zinc-galvanised corrugated steel sheets were imported into this country from Scandinavia and shortly afterwards similar sheets were produced here.

Galvanised, corrugated steel sheets are coated all over with a thin film of zinc, applied by dipping or spraying. Provided the zinc coating is sufficiently thick and adheres strongly to the steel below, it will inhibit rust for some years. On exposure the zinc coating first oxidises and then is converted to basic zinc carbonate, which is largely insoluble in clean atmospheres and protects the zinc from further corrosion. In time, however, this surface film is worn away by the scouring action of wind and rain and progressive corrosion occurs, until there is no further protection of the steel.

The principal disadvantage of corrugated steel sheets is. the difficulty of preventing corrosion of the steel for more than a few years. Other disadvantages are low thermal resistance, poor fire resistance and the poor appearance of the sheets due to the small corrugations.

Corrugated steel sheets coated with bitumen were first used in this country in 1923. During manufacture these sheets were immersed in hot bitumen which adhered strongly to the sheet and was effective in preventing corrosion of the steel for some time. However, the bitumen coating by itself was highly inflammable and some spectacular fires, during which the bitumen burned fiercely and the sheeting collapsed, caused this early type of protected sheeting to be withdrawn. A later, improved protective coating consisted of hot bitumen covered with a coating of asbestos felt bonded to the bitumen which was in turn coated with bitumen. The combination of bitumen and asbestos felt protected the steel sheets from corrosion, improved thermal resistance and provided a fair degree of resistance to damage by fire.

With improvements in the techniques of cold roll forming steel strip, a range of trapezoidal-section profiled steel sheets was introduced about 1960. The improved strength and rigidity of these profiles allowed the use of thinner strip and wider spacing of support than is possible with the shallow section of corrugated sheet, and the bold angular trapezoidal profile contrasted favourably with the small, somewhat indeterminate, profile of corrugated sheet. These trapezoidal profile sheets were at first coated with zinc, asbestos felt and bitumen and later with organic plastic coatings.

Plastic-coated profiled steel sheeting is the principal sheet material used for weather protection of single-storey framed buildings today. These sheets are made in a wide range of trapezoidal profiles and colours. Trapezoidal profile steel sheets are also the principal material used for roof decking where the sheets serve as support for insulation and a weather coat of built-up bitumen felt roofing.

Corrugated asbestos cement sheets were first used in 1910 as an alternative to corrugated steel sheets. Asbestos cement sheets, which do not suffer atmospheric corrosion, are maintenance-free and comparable in cost to steel sheets, have been much used for the roofs and walls of sheds, factories, warehouses and other single-storey framed buildings. The disadvantages of asbestos cement as a sheet covering are its dull, cement grey colour, the thickness of the sheet, which makes it impossible to make a close joint at overlap of sheets for low pitched roofs, and the brittle nature of the material, which is readily fractured during handling, fixing or in use. A range of deep profile and coloured asbestos cement sheeting is manufactured.

ROOF AND WALL SHEETING AND DECKING

The functional requirements of roofs and walls are:

Strength and stability
Exclusion of wind and rain
Thermal insulation
Durability
Sound insulation
Fire resistance and safety from fire.

Strength and stability: Most single-storey buildings are constructed with medium- or long-span steel or reinforced concrete frames to provide maximum, unobstructed, covered floor space. The tendency during the last fifty years has been to economise in materials by the use of small section frames, such as the sloping or low pitch steel portal frame, covered with thin, light-weight, profiled steel sheets with light-weight insulation either under or over the sheets.

To meet the demand for economy in first cost a range of thin, steel strip sheets has been produced in increasingly deep profiles to provide adequate strength and stiffness to support the self-weight and imposed wind and snow loads normal to walls and roofs, over increasingly wide centres of support. The depth of the profile of steel cladding and decking sheets, with longitudinal and transverse stiffening ribs, is designed to provide sufficient strength and stiffness to support the dead load of the roof or wall covering itself, wind and snow loads and the very considerable uplift forces due to wind suction that occur particularly at the eaves and verges of roofs of large buildings. Additional depth of profile with stiffening ribs and closer spacing of fasteners has been used to resist the forces due to suction from wind pressure on roofs.

Usual practice is to design the structural frame with adequate strength and stability to support the dead weight of the roof and wall covering and wind and snow loads, with systems of wind braces to stiffen the frames against the racking effect of wind, without taking into account the effect of the roof and wall covering in stiffening the frames, so that the frame and the covering are treated separately for the purpose of design.

In recent years the effect of the roof covering in providing stiffness to the structural frame has sometimes been included in the design of structural frames for large buildings.

Steel roof cladding sheets fixed across a structural frame act as a horizontal diaphragm which contributes to the stability of the frames in resisting the racking effect of the considerable lateral wind forces that act on the sides and roofs of large buildings. The extent of the contribution of the sheet covering to the stability of the frames depends on the thickness of the sheet, the depth of the profile of the sheets, the strength of the fasteners used to fix the sheets and the strength of the sheet in resisting the tearing effect of the fasteners fixed through it. From a calculation of the wind forces acting on a building, cladding sheets of adequate thickness to resist tearing away from fasteners, adequate profile to resist buckling and the required section and spacing of fasteners can be selected so that the sheeting will act in whole or part as a diaphragm to resist wind pressures on the building.

Because the saving in cost, through reduction in material, that is effected by the design of the structural frame and the covering as a whole, is small in comparison to the total cost of a building, this approach is generally limited to the design of large buildings.

Exclusion of wind and rain: The demand for large covered floor areas with the least obstruction by internal columns has led to the adoption of flat, sloping or low pitch structural frames, covered with impermeable membranes or profiled sheets, to reduce the unused roof space that has to be wastefully heated. The consequence has been many failures of large flat roofs due to the ageing fatigue of the materials used to cover flat roofs and the disruptive effects of movements due to temperature differences caused by increased thermal insulation and increased difficulties in making weathertight joints at the overlaps of roof sheets fixed to sloping and low pitch roofs.

Modifications of the materials used for flat roof coverings to improve resistance to the inevitable brittle hardening of materials exposed on roofs together with improvements in the details of fixing and at upstands, have increased the durability of flat roof coverings. Sealed joints at overlaps of sheet material to exclude wind and rain, while at the same time allowing for thermal movement, have made it possible to cover sloping and low pitch roofs with profiled sheet coverings.

Thermal insulation: The Building Regulations (First Amendment) 1978 Part FF prescribe minimum values for the insulation of floors, walls and roofs to conserve heat and fuel resources.

To meet the requirements set by the Regulations most forms of wall and roof construction have to include a layer of material used specifically for the purpose of thermal insulation. Walls and roofs covered with thin sheets, that have negligible resistance to the transfer of heat, have to incorporate in their construction a layer of some material that has good resistance to the transfer of heat. Materials that provide good resistance to the transfer of heat are fibrous, cellular or porous, have poor mechanical strength and require some form of support and protection from damage. Most of the plastic materials used for insulation have a low melting point and require some form of protective lining to provide support for the material and to afford some protection from the heat generated by fires.

The necessary inclusion of a layer of material, with a low rate of conductivity, sandwiched in the construction of wall and roof coverings, has greatly increased the range of temperature differences between the warmed inside of buildings and the seasonal and day by day variations of outside temperatures, which puts considerable strain on roof coverings laid over insulating layers and leads to the problems of corrosion and decay occasioned by condensation.

The choice of materials to be used in the construction of walls and roofs has to be a compromise of economy in the use of materials, durability, thermal insulation, resistance to damage by fire and sound insulation because no one material by itself will satisfactorily meet all the requirements.

Durability: As the initial cost and subsequent maintenance of many large single-storey buildings, such as factories and warehouses, is small in comparison to the capital outlay on machinery and the annual turnover and profit of industrial concerns, little attention is paid to the durability of the materials and construction of these buildings. Most of the materials used in single-storey industrial buildings are thin, light-weight and short-lived with a useful life of up to about twenty to thirty years before considerable work is necessary to maintain the minimum requirements of shelter and acceptable appearance.

None of the light-weight materials used for economy in the construction of walls and roofs should be expected to have the durability of the traditional materials brick, tile, slate and non-ferrous metals.

Sound insulation: Light-weight wall and roof coverings and insulation which meet the minimum requirements for thermal insulation, offer poor resistance to sound transmission. Where sound insulation is a critical requirement for walls and roofs, some solid material such as brick or concrete must be used, whose mass will afford appreciable sound reduction.

Fire resistance and safety from fire: The regulations that govern fire resistance and safety from fire are concerned with the safety of people inside buildings and their escape in case of fire.

The resistance to fire of the elements of the construction of buildings is expressed in periods of ½, 1, 1½, 2, 3, 4, and 6 hours, which are the periods of time that an element of structure performs its normal structural or separating function when subjected to the heat generated by fires, without collapse or failure to arrest the spread of fire. The period of fire resistance prescribed by regulation is related to the use of the building, its height, floor area and volume as a measure of the notional period of time that is required for the occupants of buildings to escape in safety after the beginning of a fire.

The combustibility of materials of construction is concerned with the behaviour of particular materials in fires with regard to the degree to which the material may encourage the fire or assist in the spread of the fire by its combustibility.

Fire propagation is the term used to express the degree to which a material contributes to a fire by its ignitability which is given by a numerical index of the amount and rate of heat evolved.

The spread of flame over the combustible surface of materials, particularly in walls and ceilings, can assist in the growth of fires in buildings. Materials used in building are included in four classes from Class 1 surface of very low flame spread to Class 4 surface of rapid flame spread.

The resistance of a roof to penetration by external fire, from adjacent buildings, for example, and the resistance of a roof to the spread of flame over its external surface are categorised by two letters; the first letter for resistance to penetration of fire and the second for resistance to the spread of flame. Category AA designates a roof as 'A', not penetrated within one hour and the second 'A' as having no spread of flame. The letters B, C, D denote a diminution in resistance to penetration and spread of flame.

Plastics, which have a low melting point, are classified separately from other building materials in respect of behaviour in fire.

Fire protection is concerned with the protection of a building to control or reduce damage to the building and danger to persons by the use of equipment which detects and gives warning of overheating or smoke from fires, extinguishes fires by water or foam or which contains fires by shutters, doors or vents for smoke that are operated by fusible links or stays.

The very considerable range of requirements for the resistance to fire of the elements of building and the resistance of materials to the spread of flame are determined by reference to the use of a particular building and its floor area and volume.

Profiled steel sheeting

The advantages of steel as a material for roof and wall sheeting are that its favourable strength-to-weight ratio and ductility make it both practical and economic to use comparatively thin, light-weight sheets that can be cold roll formed to profiles with adequate strength and stiffness for handling and to support the loads normal to roof and wall coverings. The disadvantages of steel as a sheeting material are that it suffers rapid, progressive corrosion and has negligible resistance to damage by fire.

The thin coated strip of steel is cold roll formed by passing the coil of steel strip through a series of rollers that progressively profile the strip longitudinally so that the ridges provide sufficient stiffness for handling, fixing and support for the anticipated loads on roofs and walls.

Corrugated steel sheet has shallow corrugations (¾ in) 19 deep that provide longitudinal strength and rigidity sufficient for the limited centres of support common in small buildings and economy in the reduction of the width of steel strip by forming. The cover width of corrugated sheet is 990.6 mm as compared to 750 for a trapezoidal profile sheet 48 deep.

The typical trapezoidal profile steel sheet is formed with trapezoidal section ridges with flat lower flanges as illustrated in Fig. 47. The depth of the ridges provides longitudinal strength and stiffness for support of dead and imposed loads. The thin flat bottom flange of the sheet between the ridges is subject to buckling in handling, fixing and local loading, such as wind uplift, to the extent that it may be necessary to improve stiffness with shallow longitudinal ribs in both the wide lower flanges and the top of the ribs, as illustrated in Fig. 47.

Of recent years deep profile sheets with a depth of up to 200 have been produced for spans of up to 12.0 between structural frames or beams without intermediate support from purlins. To prevent buckling, a wide top flange is formed with closely spaced transverse stiffening ridges and the deep webs with longitudinal stiffeners as shown in Fig. 50.

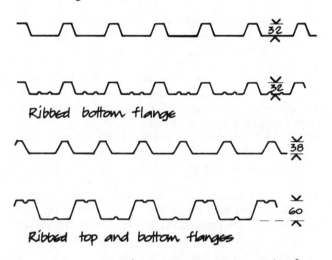

Ribbed bottom flange

Ribbed top and bottom flanges

Trapezoidal profile coated steel roofing sheets

Fig. 47

Protective coatings for profiled steel sheets

Corrosion of steel: When exposed to the action of air and water or salt solutions, steel undergoes a complex electro-chemical change which is essentially a process of oxidation, termed corrosion, where the metal tends to return to an oxidised condition similar in composition to an iron ore from which the steel was produced. The corrosive oxidation of steel produces a reddish deposit on the surface of steel, known as rust. The initial deposit of rust does not generally prevent further corrosion of the steel below so that progressive corrosion of the metal occurs. Because rust has poor strength and negligible ductility, the characteristics for which steel is used, corrosion reduces the usefulness of steel.

The corrosive process is a complex electro-chemical action that depends on the characteristics of the metal, atmosphere and temperature. Corrosion of steel is most destructive in conditions of persistent moisture, atmospheric pollution and where different metals are in contact.

Zinc coating: The most economic and effective way of protecting steel against corrosion is by coating it with zinc, which corrodes more slowly than steel. The zinc coating acts as a barrier against contact of steel with the atmosphere, and acts sacrificially to protect the steel at cut edges by galvanic action where two dissimilar metals are in contact in the presence of moisture and corrosion of only one takes place. The most reactive of the two will become the anode in a natural electric cell and will oxidise to protect the cathode from corrosion. Thus the zinc coat protects the steel as it is anodic to steel in a galvanic action and corrodes sacrificially to the benefit of the steel.

Hot-dip galvanising: This is the most commonly used method of applying a zinc coating to steel. There are three stages to the process. The steel is first degreased and cleaned in cold, dilute hydrochloric acid, the cleaned steel is given a prefluxing treatment and then fully immersed in molten zinc at a temperature of about 450°C. The thickness of the zinc coating depends on the time of immersion, withdrawal rate and the temperature of the molten zinc. Coatings of zinc are 275 g/m^2 for decking, 350 g/m^2 for cladding and 450 g/m^2 and 600 g/m^2 to provide added protection and longer life for the coated steel. The zinc coating adheres strongly to the steel through the formation of a very thin alloy layer, between the steel and the zinc, which bonds strongly to both metals.

The protection afforded by the zinc coating depends on the thickness of the coating and atmospheric conditions. The products of the corrosion of zinc in rural areas are of low solubility that tend to inhibit corrosion of the zinc below for periods of up to thirty years, whereas the products of corrosion in industrial atmospheres are soluble and afford less protection for periods of about seven years. The life expectancy of a protective zinc coating, in a particular atmosphere is proportional to the weight of the zinc coating.

In rural, dry sub-tropical and marine tropical areas, where the rate of atmospheric corrosion is low, hot-dip galvanised zinc coating will provide by itself adequate protection of steel sheets where the metallic grey colour of the sheets provides an acceptable finish to buildings.

Organically (plastic) coated profiled steel sheets: The majority of profiled steel sheets used today are organically coated with one of the plastic coatings available for the protection afforded by the plastic finish and the range of colours available. Plastic coatings to galvanised zinc coated steel sheets serve as a barrier to atmospheric corrosion of zinc, the erosive effect of wind and rain and protection from damage during handling, fixing and in use. Also they serve as a means of applying a colour to the surface of the sheets. The principal benefit of the extra cost of the plastic coating is in the application of a colour to what is otherwise a drab metallic grey zinc coating.

Colour is applied to organically coated steel sheets by the addition of pigment to the coating material. The effect of ultra-violet radiation and the weathering effect of wind and rain is to gradually bleach the colour pigment in the coating. Loss of colour is not uniform over the whole surface of profiled steel sheets, it being most pronounced on south facing slopes and sides of buildings and irregular on the ridges and flanges of the sheets. This varied loss of colour over a number of years spoils the appearance of buildings.

Organically coated steel sheets are used principally for the benefit of the colours available, so the inevitable loss of colour may in time become unacceptable from the point of view of appearance. The term 'life expectancy to first maintenance', used in relation to coloured, organically coated steel sheets, expresses the time in years that a particular coating will adequately retain its colour to a comparatively stringent standard of appearance before overpainting is deemed necessary. The term 'life expectancy' is not generally used to define the useful life of the coating as protection against corrosion and damage, which is usually considerably longer than that of colour retention.

Organic coatings for profiled steel sheets

uPVC — polyvinyl chloride: This is the cheapest and most used of the organic plastic coatings. This coating goes under the trade name 'Plastisol'. The comparatively thick (200 micron) coating, which is applied over a zinc coating, provides good resistance to damage in handling, fixing and in use and good resistance to normal weathering agents. The material is UV stabilised to retard degradation by ultra-violet light and the consequent chalking and loss of colour. The durability of the coating is good as a protection for the zinc coating below but the life expectancy to first maintenance of acceptable colour retention is only of the order of ten to twenty years.

Polyvinyl chloride is an economic, tough, durable, scratch-resistant coating that will provide good protection of the zinc coating and steel below for many years but has poor colour retention.

Acrylic — polymethyl methacrylate — PMMA: This organic plastic, which is about twice the price of uPVC, is applied with heat under pressure as a laminate to galvanised zinc steel strip to a thickness of 75 microns. It forms a tough finish with high strength, good impact resistance and good resistance to damage in handling, fixing and in use. It has excellent chemical resistance and its good resistance to ultra-violet radiation gives a life expectancy of acceptable colour retention to first maintenance of up to twenty years. The hard smooth finish of this coating is particularly free from dirt staining.

PVDF — polyvinylidene fluoride: A comparatively expensive organic plastic coating for profiled steel sheets which is used as a thin (25 micron) coating to zinc coated steel strip for its excellent resistance to weathering, excellent chemical resistance, durability and resistance to all high energy radiation. Because the coating is thin it may be damaged by careless handling and fixing. The durability of this coating is good as a protection for the zinc coating and the steel sheet and its life expectancy to first maintenance in relation to colour retention is better than fifteen years and up to thirty years.

Silicone polyester: This is the cheapest of the coloured organic coatings used for galvanised steel sheet. It is suitable for use in temperate climates where its life expectancy to first maintenance is from five to seven years. It is not suitable for use in marine, hot humid atmospheres or where there is aggressive industrial pollution of the atmosphere. The galvanised steel sheets are primed and coated with stoved silicone polyester to a thickness of 25 micron. The coating provides reasonable protection against damage in handling, fixing and in use, good resis-

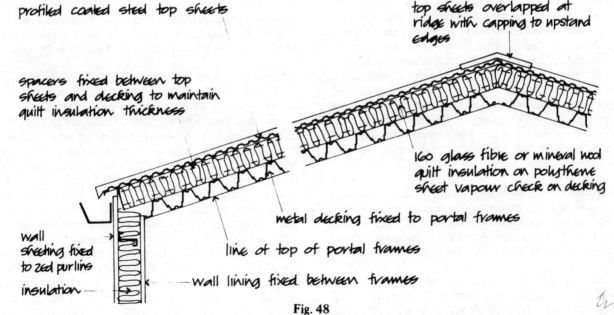

profiled coated steel top sheets

top sheets overlapped at ridge with capping to upstand edges

spacers fixed between top sheets and decking to maintain quilt insulation thickness

160 glass fibre or mineral wool quilt insulation on polythene sheet vapour check on decking

metal decking fixed to portal frames

wall sheeting fixed to zed purlins

line of top of portal frames

insulation

wall lining fixed between frames

Fig. 48

tance to ultra-violet radiation and a life expectancy to first maintenance of five to seven years.

Bitumen and asbestos coatings: Galvanised steel strip is coated with hot bitumen, a second layer of a composite of asbestos and bitumen and finished with a coloured alkyd resin. This coating provides good protection against corrosion, moderate protection against damage in handling, fixing and in use and a life expectancy of ten to fifteen years to first maintenance.

Profiled steel cladding and decking

Cladding: Thin sheets of steel provide negligible resistance to the transfer of heat to the extent that some material has to be fixed either under or over the sheets to serve as a barrier to excessive transfer of heat. The term 'cladding' is used to describe sheets, exposed as the external envelope of a structure, which provide protection against wind and rain and which support their own weight and the loads imposed by wind and snow. Cladding for roofs is known as roof sheeting or roof cladding, and cladding for walls as wall sheeting, walling or sidewalling. Because cladding serves as a weathering skin, insulation has to be laid or fixed under it as illustrated in Fig. 48.

Decking: This is the term used for profiled sheeting that supports the weight of insulation and a weathering surface of bitumen felt or asphalt in addition to its self-weight and the imposed loads of wind and snow. The insulation is laid on and supported by the decking as illustrated in Fig. 49.

Materials that are effective as insulation against transfer of heat are light-weight, porous, have poor mechanical strength and need to be given support at close intervals. When fixed under cladding, insulation is either laid over roof purlins or supported on metal angle framing hung from the purlins. The need for comparatively close centres of support for insulation imposes severe limitations on the centres of support for profiled steel sheet cladding. But for the need to give support to insulation, there is no theoretical limit to the depth of profile of sheets and the unsupported span of the sheets.

In practice steel sheet cladding can have deep profiles capable of providing adequate strength and stiffness for the sheets, by themselves, to span up to 12.0, but this would involve the use of very deep uneconomic supports for the insulation below. For this reason the practical limit of the unsupported span of roof cladding, with over-purlin insulating lining, is about 4.0, to provide an economic span for the supports necessary for insulation.

Because decking provides support for insulation, its unsupported span is not limited by the need to provide separate support to the structurally weak insulation material, and spans of up to 12.0 are possible. This, the principal advantage of decking over cladding, may obviate the need for the use of intermediate supports between structural frames or beams with the decking spanning between portal frames or main beams on a low-pitch, sloping or flat roof. Some comparative profiles of steel cladding and decking are illustrated in Fig. 50.

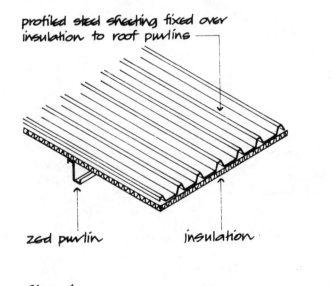

profiled steel sheeting fixed over insulation to roof purlins

zed purlin   insulation

Cladding

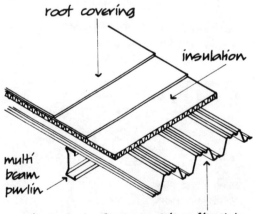

roof covering

insulation

multi beam purlin

profiled steel sheet decking fixed to purlins or roof frames supports insulation and root covering

Root decking

Fig. 49

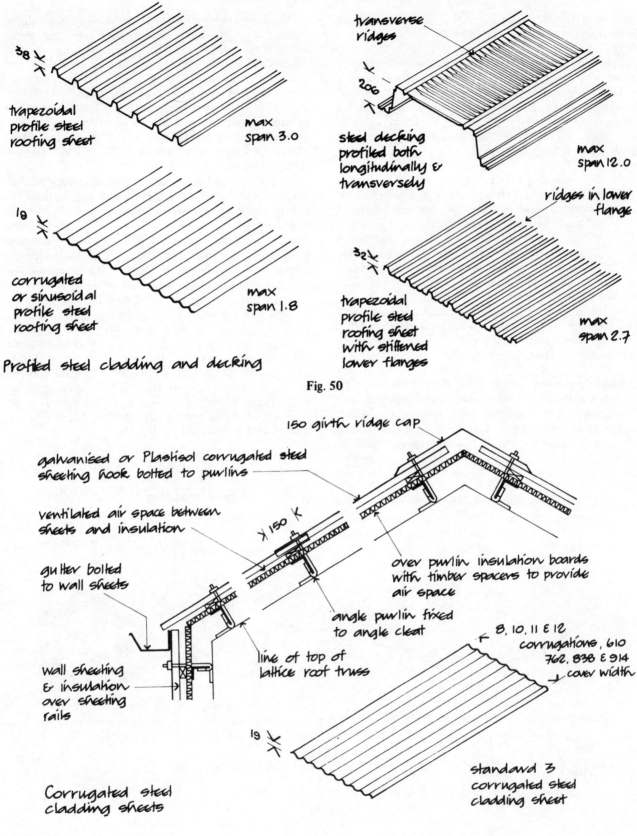

trapezoidal profile steel roofing sheet

38

max span 3.0

corrugated or sinusoidal profile steel roofing sheet

19

max span 1.8

Profiled steel cladding and decking

transverse ridges

steel decking profiled both longitudinally & transversely

206

max span 12.0

ridges in lower flange

trapezoidal profile steel roofing sheet with stiffened lower flanges

32

max span 2.7

Fig. 50

150 girth ridge cap

galvanised or Plastisol corrugated steel sheeting hook bolted to purlins

ventilated air space between sheets and insulation

150

gutter bolted to wall sheets

over purlin insulation boards with timber spacers to provide air space

angle purlin fixed to angle cleat

wall sheeting & insulation over sheeting rails

line of top of lattice roof truss

Corrugated steel cladding sheets

8, 10, 11 & 12 corrugations, 610 762, 838 & 914 cover width

19

standard 3 corrugated steel cladding sheet

Fig. 51

32

Profiled steel cladding: Fig. 47 is an illustration of typical profiled steel cladding sheets.

Corrugated sheets: Corrugated steel sheets are little used in this country, other than for small structures and shelters for agricultural and storage purposes, because of the limited unsupported spans possible and the appearance of the shallow sinusoidal corrugations that do not provide the pronounced shading effect of angular trapezoidal profile sheets. The shallow profile of the corrugations makes for the least reduction in the width of steel strip during profiling and the most economic cover width of all the profiled sheets.

Fig. 51 is an illustration of a symmetrical pitch roof covered with corrugated steel sheet fixed to angle purlins with galvanised hook bolts which are in turn fixed in the ridges of the corrugations and hooked around the purlins.

The sheets are fixed with end laps of at least 150 and side laps of one corrugation. The pitch of the roof should be not less than 10 degrees to the horizontal to exclude wind and rain. Purlins are spaced at from 1.0 to 2.0 centres.

From Fig. 51 it will be seen that the roof and walls are insulated by laying insulation boards over the purlins and sheeting rails. This system of over purlin insulation is the most economic method of supporting insulation on closely spaced purlins, as the purlins support both the cladding and the insulation. As a barrier or check to warm, moist air, the insulation boards should be lined on their underside with an impermeable covering. This covering serves as a vapour check against moist, warm air penetrating the insulation layer and there should be a ventilated air space between the insulation and the steel sheets to minimise the possibility of warm most air condensing on the underside of the steel sheets and so encouraging corrosion.

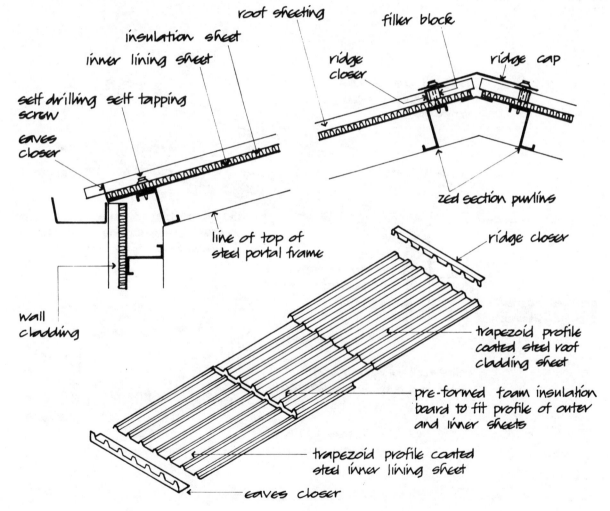

Profiled steel cladding, insulation and inner lining sheets

Fig. 52

Trapezoidal profile cladding: Fig. 52 is an illustration of trapezoidal profile steel cladding with pre-formed foam insulation and profiled steel lining sheets fixed to zed purlins on a steel framed structure. This composite cladding system comprises a sandwich of cladding sheets and pre-formed insulation supported on profiled steel inner lining sheets which serve as a vapour check and provide a smooth, painted soffit.

The composite cladding is secured to the zed purlins with self-drilling, self-tapping fasteners fixed in the troughs of the cladding sheets with 150 minimum end laps and one ridge side lap. The roof cladding should be fixed to a minimum pitch of 10 degrees to the horizontal. Cold-formed steel ridge, eaves and angle flashings are fixed through profiled plastic filler blocks.

The advantages of this composite cladding system are economy in fixing as over-purlin insulation and a neat, smooth pre-finished soffit lining.

Fig. 53 is an illustration of trapezoid profile steel cladding sheets fixed to zed purlins with fibre insulation laid on top of lining boards which are supported by metal 'T' bars hung from the purlins as under-purlin insulation. The profiled cladding sheets are fixed to the purlins with self-drilling, self-tapping fasteners on a roof pitched at a minimum of 10 degrees to the horizontal. The air space between the roof cladding and the insulation is ventilated to reduce the likelihood of warm, moist air condensing on the underside of the cold steel cladding sheets.

The under-purlin insulation system allows a considerable thickness of fibre insulation to give good insulation against transfer of heat, and the lining boards supporting the insulation provide a smooth, level finish to the soffit.

Under-purlin insulation is more expensive than over-purlin insulation because of the additional labour and materials involved in the support of the insulation separately from the cladding.

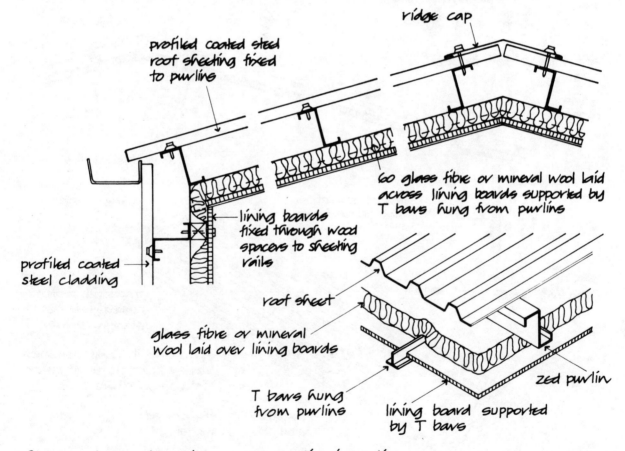

Steel roof sheeting with under purlin insulation

Fig. 53

34

Fasteners: Profiled steel sheet cladding is fixed to purlins and sheeting rails with self-drilling, self-tapping screws driven by power operated tools through the troughs of the cladding sheets and the top flange of zed or multi-beam purlins and rails in one operation. The fasteners are fitted with a weatherseal washer, composed of a dished metal washer and a neoprene washer, which is clamped firmly to the sheets to exclude rain. Fig. 54 is an illustration of a typical fastener. Various lengths of fastener are available to accommodate over-purlin insulation, fixing at overlaps of sheet and direct fixing to purlins. These fasteners are fixed in the troughs of profiled sheets, through the lower flange rather than through the upstand ridges where the self-drilling operation is liable to damage the flimsy sheet material.

For fixing to hot-rolled angle or channel purlins and rails self-tapping fasteners are used. A hole is first drilled through the sheet and the thick material of the angle or channel. A self-tapping fastener is then driven into the hole with a power operated tool. Fig. 54 is an illustration of self-drilling and self-tapping, and self-tapping fasteners and weatherseal washers.

Profiled steel decking: Trapezoidal profile steel decking is hot-dip galvanised and zinc coated on both faces for protection against corrosion. The zinc coating provides adequate protection and is the usual finish where the metallic grey of the zinc coat is an acceptable finish to the underside of exposed decking. As an alternative the underside of the decking may be primed ready for painting or coated with a paint finish. Fig. 55 is an illustration of some typical steel decking sections.

Profiled steel decking is used as the support for insulation and a weather finish of built-up bitumen felt for flat, sloping and low pitch roofs for the advantage of widely spaced supports that is possible with deep profile decking.

The trapezoid profile steel decking illustrated in Fig. 56 is fixed to the secondary beams of a flat roof structure with self-tapping fasteners. A felt vapour check is bonded to the decking with bitumen. Insulation boards are bonded to the vapour check either with bitumen or self-drilling, self-tapping fasteners and flat washers as necessary to resist wind suction uplift. The roof is finished with built-up bitumen felt as a weathering surface.

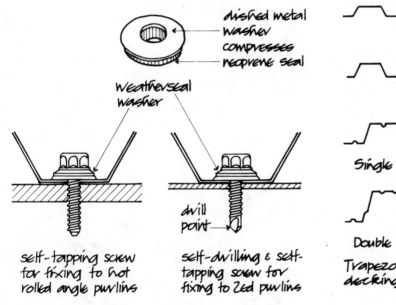

dished metal washer compresses neoprene seal

weatherseal washer

self-tapping screw for fixing to hot rolled angle purlins

drill point

self-drilling & self-tapping screw for fixing to Zed purlins

Fasteners for profiled steel sheeting and decking

Fig. 54

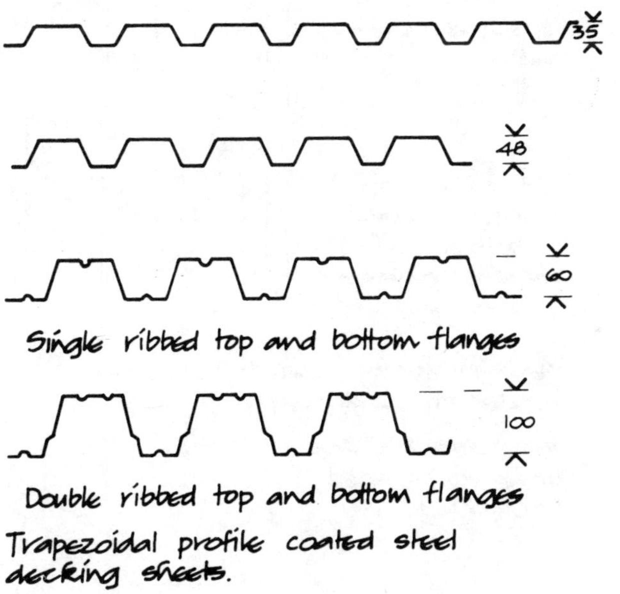

35
Single ribbed top and bottom flanges

Double ribbed top and bottom flanges

Trapezoidal profile coated steel decking sheets.

Fig. 55

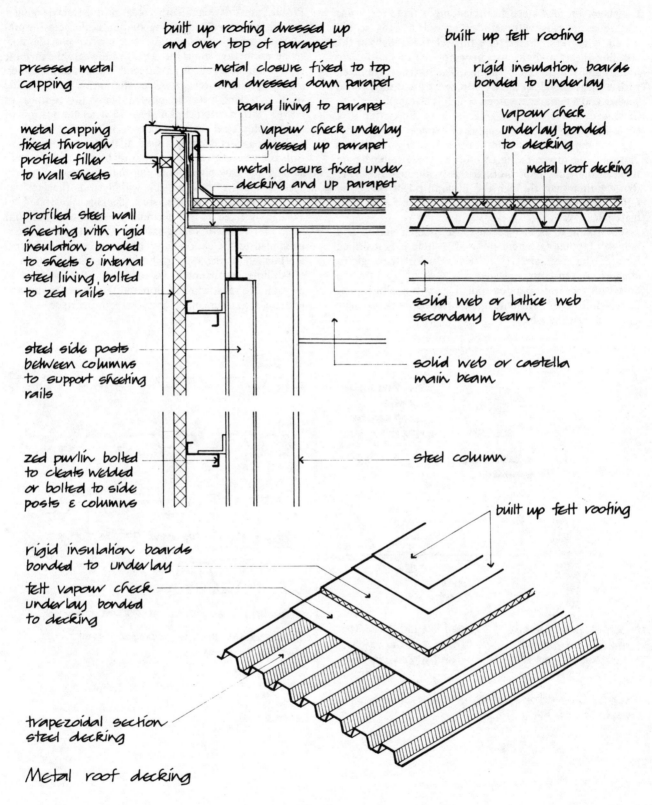

pressed metal capping

metal capping fixed through profiled filler to wall sheets

profiled steel wall sheeting with rigid insulation bonded to sheets & internal steel lining, bolted to zed rails

steel side posts between columns to support sheeting rails

zed purlin bolted to cleats welded or bolted to side posts & columns

built up roofing dressed up and over top of parapet

metal closure fixed to top and dressed down parapet

board lining to parapet

vapour check underlay dressed up parapet

metal closure fixed under decking and up parapet

built up felt roofing

rigid insulation boards bonded to underlay

vapour check underlay bonded to decking

metal roof decking

solid web or lattice web secondary beam

solid web or castella main beam

steel column

rigid insulation boards bonded to underlay

felt vapour check underlay bonded to decking

built up felt roofing

trapezoidal section steel decking

Metal roof decking

Fig. 56

36

Composite steel decking and cladding: This is a roofing system which combines the long span advantages of steel decking, a high degree of insulation and profiled steel cladding for low pitch roofs, as illustrated in Fig. 57. The profiled steel decking has deep webs stiffened longitudinally for spans of up to 12.0, for fixing between widely spaced beams or roof frames without intermediate support. Lattice steel spacer bars are fixed to the decking over a polythene vapour check to accommodate a thick layer of fibre insulation. The profiled PVF or acrylic coated steel cladding sheets are supported by the spacer bars under the longitudinal ridges of the cladding which has shallow transverse stiffening ribs to strengthen the wide bottom flange of the profile.

This roofing system is designed specifically for the high insulation value of the comparatively thick layer of fibre insulation that is possible due to the spacer bars and the life expectancy to first maintenance of the PVF or acrylic coating. Fibre insulation finished thicknesses of 160, 220 or 270 are available with this roof system.

Profiled steel wall cladding

Corrugated or trapezoidal profile coated steel sheets are used as wall cladding to the side and end walls of pitched and flat roof structures with insulation and inner lining sheets, the method of fixing being the same as that for roof cladding. Profiled roof cladding sheets or one of the side wall cladding profiled sections designed specifically for walling, illustrated in Fig. 58, may be used. The profiled sheets can be fixed with the ridges vertical or the ridges horizontal or a combination of both, in panels, to break up long wall surfaces. Where the sheets are fixed with the ridges vertical they are fixed to zed, multi-beam, angle or channel section sheeting rails fixed to the posts, or columns of the structural frame as in Fig. 59. The composite system of cladding, pre-formed insulation and inner lining sheets is used for both the roof and the side walling (Fig. 59). Where the wall cladding is fixed with the ridges of the sheets horizontal it is either necessary to fix sheeting posts in between the structural columns or fix a double system of rails and posts. Intermediate rails of

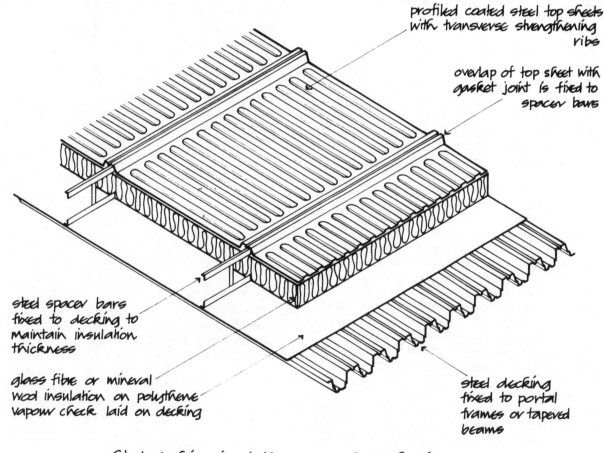

profiled coated steel top sheets with transverse strengthening ribs

overlap of top sheet with gasket joint is fixed to spacer bars

steel spacer bars fixed to decking to maintain insulation thickness

glass fibre or mineral wool insulation on polythene vapour check laid on decking

steel decking fixed to portal frames or tapered beams

Steel decking insulation and steel sheeting

Fig. 57

angle, channel or top-hat section are fixed across the structural frame as a support for zed or multi-beam sheeting rails that are fixed vertically as support for the horizontally fixed sheets.

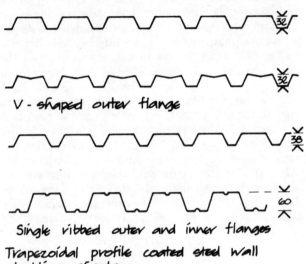

V - shaped outer flange

Single ribbed outer and inner flanges

Trapezoidal profile coated steel wall cladding sheets

Fig. 58

The brick and block cavity wall, illustrated in Fig. 59, is built on reinforced concrete ground beams bearing on the pad foundations of the structural columns or posts. The solid, robust brick and block wall, which can suffer damage more readily than the comparatively flimsy steel cladding, is raised some few feet above the level of the floor.

The loads on the foundations of single-storey buildings are small in comparison to the safe bearing capacity of most natural subsoils. A mass concrete pad foundation for structural columns is generally adequate to the support of the loads from the columns or posts of single-storey buildings on natural undisturbed subsoil. On subsoils with poor bearing capacity or on made-up ground or where there are appreciable variations in the safe bearing capacity of the subsoil, a system of pile foundations with pile caps is carried down to a firm stratum or a reinforced concrete raft is cast over the area of the building with downstand or upstand ground beams to support columns and walls.

Where profiled cladding is used as wall cladding it is practice to form a brick or concrete upstand above the level of the floor on to which the sheeting is finished. The upstand serves as a fixing and finish for the drip and flashing on to which the sheeting is finished and as a support and fixing for sheeting posts fixed between main structural columns or posts.

Because of the disturbance of subsoil caused by the excavations for the foundations of columns it is not wise to build or cast upstands for walls directly off the floor because of the possibility of some settlement movement

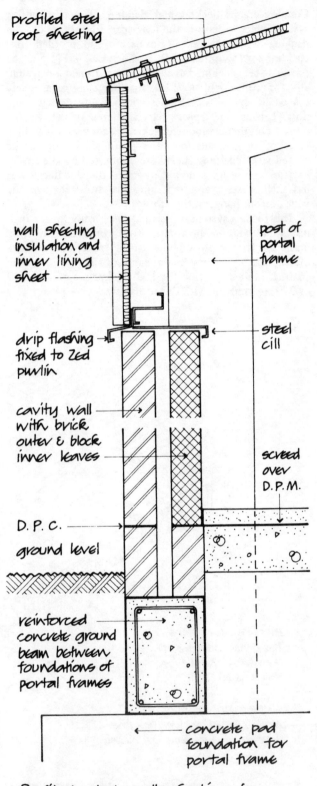

profiled steel roof sheeting

wall sheeting insulation and inner lining sheet

drip flashing fixed to Zed purlin

cavity wall with brick outer & block inner leaves

D.P.C.
ground level

reinforced concrete ground beam between foundations of portal frames

post of portal frame

steel cill

screed over D.P.M.

concrete pad foundation for portal frame

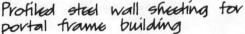

Profiled steel wall sheeting for portal frame building

Fig. 59

around columns. The concrete curb or the base for a brick upstand should be formed either on a strip foundation between column bases or formed as a reinforced concrete ground beam between column bases as illustrated in Fig. 59.

There are no statutory requirements for the insulation of ground floors against transfer of heat to the ground below. All concrete floors should be constructed with a damp-proof membrane (d.p.m.) sandwiched in the construction and continued up and out to overlap the d.p.c., in walls, to prevent the damp, cold-under-foot conditions caused by the damp surface of a concrete floor without a damp-proof membrane. The inclusion of a layer of insulation, over the damp-proof membrane and under the concrete, is advisable to conserve heat and provide a warm comfortable floor surface. One of the closed cell insulation materials, such as expanded glass boards, is used.

Contoured (curved) profiled steel cladding sheets: As a finish for eaves, ridges and angles, contoured profiled steel cladding sheets are cold roll formed to a radius curve, longitudinal to the ridges of the sheets. These contoured sheets provide a curved finish to eaves, ridges and angles in place of eaves, ridge and angle flashings, so that the profile of the wall and roof sheets can be continuous as illustrated in Fig. 60. There is no economic or weathering advantage in the use of these contoured sheets; they are used solely for the sake of appearance. A consequence of the use of contoured sheets at the eaves of buildings is that there is no eaves gutter to collect the run-off of rain water from pitched roofs. The appreciable volume of rain water that will run off from a wide span roof with contoured eaves sheets is discharged down the face of the wall cladding and on to the ground. This considerable amount of water

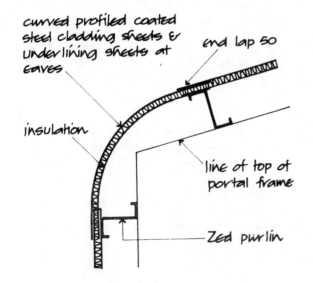

curved profiled coated steel cladding sheets & underlining sheets at eaves

end lap 50

insulation

line of top of portal frame

Zed purlin

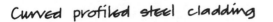

Curved profiled steel cladding

Fig. 60

will make the wall cladding more vulnerable to penetration of rain and necessitate some form of drainage channel around the building.

Most of the profiled coated steel cladding sheets can be contoured to a radius of not less than 560.

Aluminium cladding
In common with other metals, aluminium, on exposure to atmosphere, corrodes to form a thin coating of oxide on the surface. This oxide coating, which is integral with the aluminium, adheres strongly and, being insoluble, protects the metal below from further corrosion so that the useful life of aluminium is forty years or more.

Aluminium is a light-weight, malleable metal with moderate mechanical strength which can be cold formed without damage. Aluminium alloy strip is cold rolled as corrugated and trapezoid profile sheets for roof and wall cladding. The sheets are supplied as metal mill finish, metal stucco embossed finish, pre-painted or organically coated.

Mill finish is the natural untreated surface of the metal from the rolling mill. It has a smooth, highly reflective metallic, silver finish which dulls and darkens with time. Variations in the flat surfaces of the mill finish sheet will be emphasised by the reflective surface.

A stucco embossed finish to sheets is produced by embossing the sheets with rollers to form a shallow, irregular, raised patterned finish that reduces direct reflection and sun glare and so masks variations in the level of the surface of the sheet.

A painted finish is provided by coating the surface of the sheet with a passivity primer and a semi-gloss acrylic or alkyd-amino coating in a wide range of colours.

A two coat PVF_2 acrylic finish to the sheet is applied by roller to produce a low-gloss coating in a wide range of colours.

Because the somewhat dull metallic silver grey of aluminium may not provide an acceptable finish to buildings, a range of coloured coatings to aluminium sheets is supplied solely for appearance, as the aluminium sheet by itself has adequate resistance to corrosion in relation to the life of most buildings.

Aluminium cladding sheets are produced in a range of corrugated and trapezoid profiles similar to the profiles of steel sheets. Because of its poor mechanical strength, profiled aluminium sheet requires support at close centres of from 1.0 to 3.0.

Fig. 61 is an illustration of profiled aluminium cladding to the pitched roof and side walls of a framed structure. The cladding is used as a composite system of cladding, rigid plastic insulation and either steel or aluminium inner lining trays fixed as over-purlin insulation to zed purlins and zed sheeting rails. A comprehensive range of aluminium flashings is supplied for finishes at ridges, eaves, angles and openings.

Roof cladding should be fixed to a slope of not less than 12 degrees to the horizontal with end laps to sheets

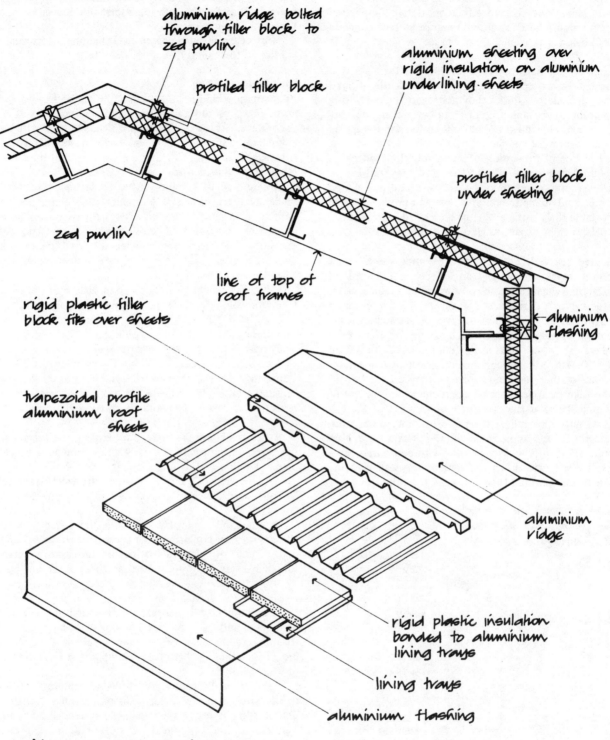

aluminium ridge bolted through filler block to zed purlin

profiled filler block

aluminium sheeting over rigid insulation on aluminium underlining sheets

profiled filler block under sheeting

zed purlin

line of top of roof frames

rigid plastic filler block fits over sheets

aluminium flashing

trapezoidal profile aluminium roof sheets

aluminium ridge

rigid plastic insulation bonded to aluminium lining trays

lining trays

aluminium flashing

Aluminium roof sheeting

Fig. 61

of at least 150 and side laps of one ridge of the profile. To allow for the considerable thermal expansion of aluminium it is practice to fix only the over sheet at end laps. To isolate the aluminium from steel purlins and sheeting rails, a barrier tape of plastic or bitumen felt is fitted between steel purlins and rails and the aluminium sheets.

Aluminium cladding is fixed with self-tapping or self-drilling, self-tapping fasteners either to the ridges or the lower flanges of the sheets. Over-purlin insulation or under-purlin insulation systems are used with profiled aluminium cladding just as they are for profiled steel sheets.

Asbestos cement cladding

Asbestos: This is a light-weight, fibrous mineral found in igneous rock formations. It is non-conducting and remains stable at high temperatures. By itself it is used for insulation and fire protection.

In 1890 a process of combining asbestos and cement to form rigid, light-weight sheets was patented. In 1910 the first corrugated asbestos cement sheets were imported into this country and soon after were manufactured here.

Asbestos cement is manufactured by felting asbestos fibres with alternate layers of cement and water. The wet mix of asbestos and cement is pressed into flat, corrugated or troughed sheets which are steam cured to accelerate hardening of the cement. The long asbestos fibres serve to reinforce the cement against tensile stresses.

Asbestos cement is hard and brittle with poor resistance to damage by knocks. It is non-combustible and liable to shatter in intense heat. It is non-corrosive, unaffected by atmospheric pollution and has a useful life of about forty years. The drab, light grey, cement colour of the sheets does not make an attractive finish to buildings. Profiled sheets tend to weather with irregular dirt staining on the sides of corrugations and troughs and algae and lichen growth may flourish on the surface of the sheets fixed at a low pitch in persistently damp conditions.

Because of the necessary thickness of the material it is not possible to make a close fitting watertight joint between sheets at laps on low pitch roofs, and the fittings to ridges and eaves look somewhat lumpy and ugly as compared to the neat finish possible with thinner steel strip.

A range of coloured asbestos cement sheets is available. The colour is applied through an acrylic coating. The life expectancy to first maintenance of the coatings is up to twenty years.

Corrugated asbestos cement sheets: These have been extensively used as a cladding for agricultural, storage and factory buildings as an economic, maintenance-free roof and wall cladding material where appearance is not a prime consideration. Of recent years coloured, coated profiled steel sheets have largely replaced asbestos cement sheets as the principal cladding material.

Two depths of corrugation are made, the traditional standard three (3″ pitch of corrugation) and the deeper

standard six (6″ pitch of corrugation) sheets illustrated in Fig. 62. In addition a troughed profile with a flat lower flange between curved ridges and a deeper profile troughed sheet with narrow lower flanges are produced as illustrated in Fig. 66. The troughed profiles are used mainly for appearance sake as the profiles provide a bolder outline than the soft sinusoidal curve of corrugated sheets.

A range of fittings is made for finishes at ridge, eaves and angles, profiled to fit the standard sheets. Fig. 63 is an illustration of ridge and eaves fittings made for corrugated sheet.

Fig. 64 shows corrugated asbestos cement sheets fixed as roof and wall cladding to a single-storey structure. The sheets are fixed without insulation over an unheated building. Insulation can be provided as either over-purlin or under-purlin insulation in the same way that insulation is provided for steel sheets.

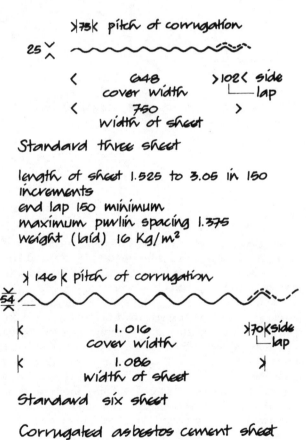

length of sheet 1.225 to 3.05 in 150 increments
end lap 150 minimum
maximum purlin spacing 925
weight (laid) 15 Kg/m²

75 pitch of corrugation
25
648 cover width
750 width of sheet
102 side lap
Standard three sheet

length of sheet 1.525 to 3.05 in 150 increments
end lap 150 minimum
maximum purlin spacing 1.375
weight (laid) 16 Kg/m²

146 pitch of corrugation
54
1.016 cover width
1.086 width of sheet
70 side lap
Standard six sheet

Corrugated asbestos cement sheet

Fig. 62

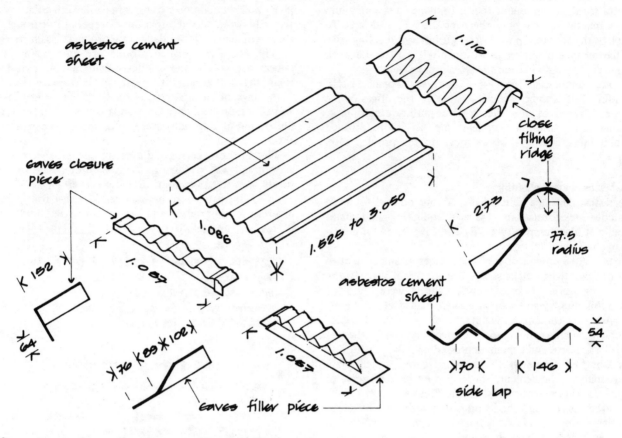

asbestos cement sheet

1.116

close tilting ridge

eaves closure piece

152

1.089

1.086

1.525 to 3.050

273

77.5 radius

64

76 89 102

1.087

asbestos cement sheet

54

70 146

side lap

eaves filler piece

Corrugated asbestos cement sheet

Fig. 63

The cladding sheets are fixed to roofs pitched at not less than 15 degrees to the horizontal with 150 end laps and one-corrugation side laps. The sheets are secured with galvanised steel hook bolts as illustrated in Fig. 64.

Fig. 66 is an illustration of the use of troughed (bold) profile asbestos cement sheets fixed to cold formed multi-span purlins on a portal frame structure with over-purlin insulation of glass fibre laid on galvanised steel lining sheets as support and finish to soffit. The glass fibre insulation is laid over the roof and down the walls as a continuous insulation lining. The lining sheets serve as support for the fibre insulation, as a vapour check and provide a smooth, level soffit to the roof and as a lining to the walls.

The thickness of the glass fibre insulation is maintained over the purlins and sheeting rails by the use of 'Z' section cold formed, galvanised steel spacers fixed to the purlins

and rails. A cranked, profiled ridge sheet weathers the ridge and an eaves closer, profiled to the sheets, acts as weathering and drip at eaves. The sheets are fixed with claw bolts to the spacers. Fig. 65 is an illustration of the fixings used for asbestos cement sheets.

Wood wool, timber and concrete decking
Wood wool slabs: These are made from seasoned wood fibres bound together under pressure with Portland cement. The finished slabs, which have coarse, open-textured surfaces, moderate compressive strength and thermal resistance and good resistance to rot and fungal growth, are used as roof deck for flat roofs to support roof coverings and provide some degree of insulation. Wood wool slabs are made in thicknesses of 50 and 75 and widths of 600 either as plain slabs or channel interlocking slabs. The material of the slabs is combustible, but not

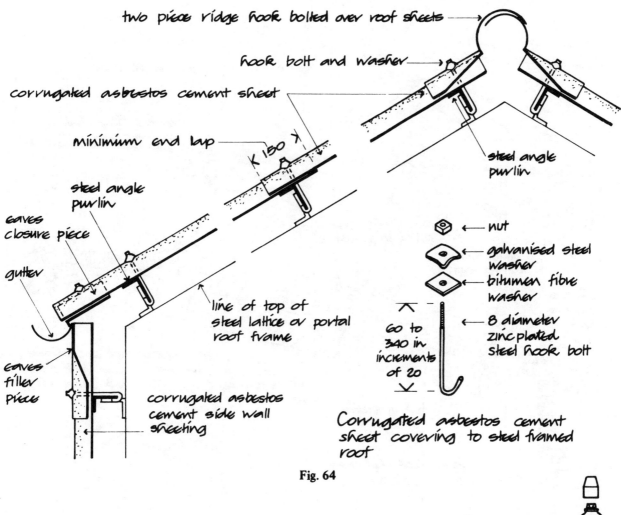

two piece ridge hook bolted over roof sheets

hook bolt and washer

corrugated asbestos cement sheet

minimum end lap

K 150

steel angle purlin

steel angle purlin

eaves closure piece

gutter

line of top of steel lattice or portal roof frame

eaves filler piece

corrugated asbestos cement side wall sheeting

nut

galvanised steel washer

bitumen fibre washer

60 to 340 in increments of 20

8 diameter zinc plated steel hook bolt

Corrugated asbestos cement sheet covering to steel framed roof

Fig. 64

readily ignited, and spread of flame is low. Plain slabs are used as a deck to timber framed roofs with the slabs supported at up to 610 centres. Slabs with cold formed reinforcing T or I sections are used across secondary beams for flat roofs, for spans of up to 2.2 and 3.0 respectively.

Tee-section cold formed steel supports are fixed with clips and plates that are screwed, welded or shot fired into purlins or secondary beams and the wood wool slabs are laid between the tee sections as illustrated in Fig. 67. The joints between the slabs are covered with hessian scrim in a slurry of cement and sand. Insulation board can be bonded or screwed to the slabs to provide additional insulation and as a base for the roof covering.

The I-section cold formed steel supports for slabs fit to grooves cut in the long edges of slabs. The supports are fixed to each supporting beam by screwing, welding or shot firing. The joints between the slabs are covered with hessian scrim in a sand and cement slurry as shown in Fig. 68.

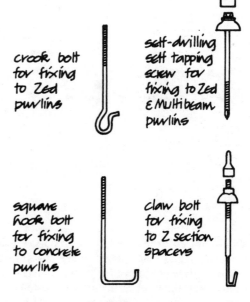

crook bolt for fixing to Zed purlins

self-drilling self tapping screw for fixing to Zed E Multibeam purlins

square hook bolt for fixing to concrete purlins

claw bolt for fixing to Z section spacers

Fixings for asbestos cement sheets

Fig. 65

43

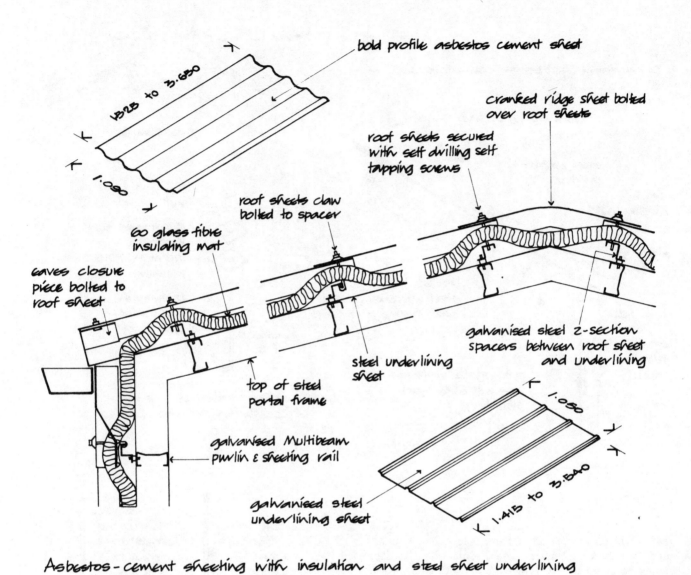

bold profile asbestos cement sheet

1.325 to 3.650

1.080

cranked ridge sheet bolted over roof sheets

roof sheets secured with self drilling self tapping screws

roof sheets claw bolted to spacer

60 glass fibre insulating mat

eaves closure piece bolted to roof sheet

galvanised steel z-section spacers between roof sheet and underlining

steel underlining sheet

top of steel portal frame

galvanised Multibeam purlin & sheeting rail

1.050

galvanised steel underlining sheet

1.415 to 3.540

Asbestos-cement sheeting with insulation and steel sheet underlining

Fig. 66

A disadvantage of the steel section supports for slabs is that they will act as cold bridges to the transfer of heat and may encourage condensation on the underside of the steel or pattern staining when the soffit is plastered.

To provide a fall for roof drainage the slabs can be laid across taper or sloping beams, or a screed to falls can be spread over the surface of the slabs, or taper section insulation can be laid across the slabs fixed to flat roofs.

Timber decking: The advantage of the use of timber beams as the structural deck for flat roofs is that timber requires no maintenance and does not suffer corrosion in humid atmospheres such as, for example, in swimming pools. Because the maximum span of timber beams is about 15.0 and the beams are more expensive than comparable standard lattice steel beams, the use of timber beams is generally limited to medium span flat roof structures where conditions such as humid atmospheres justify their use.

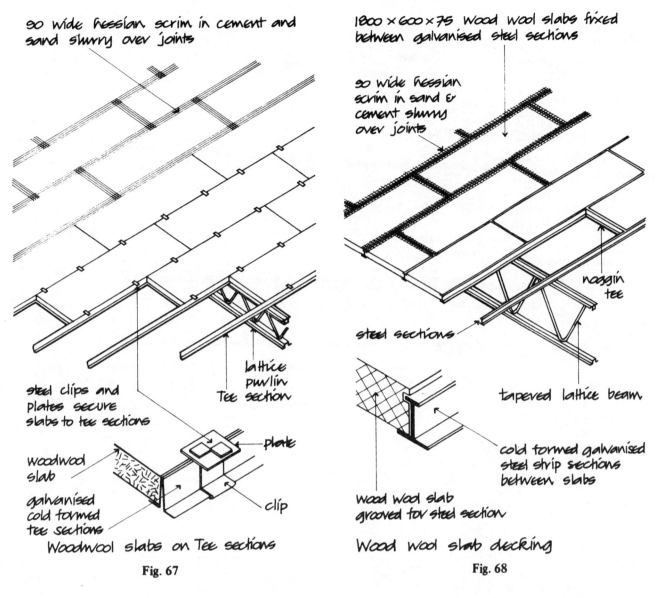

90 wide hessian scrim in cement and sand slurry over joints

steel clips and plates secure slabs to tee sections

woodwool slab

galvanised cold formed tee sections

lattice purlin Tee section

plate

clip

Woodwool slabs on Tee sections

Fig. 67

1800 × 600 × 75 wood wool slabs fixed between galvanised steel sections

90 wide hessian scrim in sand & cement slurry over joints

noggin tee

steel sections

tapered lattice beam

cold formed galvanised steel strip sections between slabs

wood wool slab grooved for steel section

Wood wool slab decking

Fig. 68

The timber beam deck illustrated in Fig. 69 consists of timber beams fabricated with plywood webs and softwood section top and bottom booms glued together with timber web stiffeners and noggin pieces. The beams are fixed at centres to suit wood wool slabs that serve as surface to the deck and insulation. To meet the requirements of The Building Regulations an additional layer of insulation is laid on the slabs or a light-weight screed can be used for additional insulation and to provide falls for drainage. The beams can be exposed or lined with plasterboard on the soffit.

Light-weight concrete slab decking: Light-weight reinforced concrete slabs are made from a mix of Portland cement, finely ground sand and lime. The materials are mixed with water and a trace of aluminium powder is

added. The mix is cast in moulds around reinforcing bars and autoclaved to cure and harden the slabs. The effect of the trace of aluminium powder is to entrain minute bubbles of gas in the aerated concrete which is lightweight and has better resistance to transfer of heat than dense concrete. The light-weight slabs are designed specifically for use as deck material for roofs where the resistance to damage by fire is an advantage.

The slabs are laid across steel or concrete flat roof structures or as a deck to concrete portal frames as illustrated in Fig. 70. The slabs are secured with steel straps cast into or fixed to the structure and reinforced with continuity steel reinforcement bedded in the joints. The slabs can be used by themselves as a deck for roof coverings or with a layer of insulation.

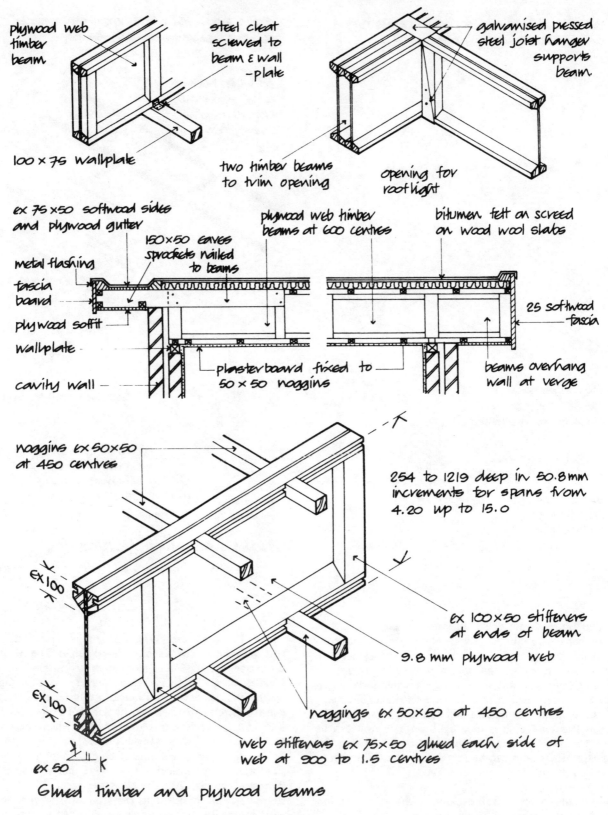

plywood web timber beam

steel cleat screwed to beam & wall -plate

galvanised pressed steel joist hanger supports beam.

100 × 75 wallplate

two timber beams to trim opening

opening for rooflight

ex 75 × 50 softwood sides and plywood gutter

150 × 50 eaves sprockets nailed to beams

plywood web timber beams at 600 centres

bitumen felt on screed on wood wool slabs

metal flashing

fascia board

plywood soffit

wallplate

cavity wall

plasterboard fixed to 50 × 50 noggins

25 softwood fascia

beams overhang wall at verge

noggins ex 50 × 50 at 450 centres

254 to 1219 deep in 50.8mm increments for spans from 4.20 up to 15.0

EX 100

EX 100

EX 50

ex 100 × 50 stiffeners at ends of beam

9.8 mm plywood web

noggings ex 50 × 50 at 450 centres

web stiffeners ex 75 × 50 glued each side of web at 900 to 1.5 centres

Glued timber and plywood beams

Fig. 69

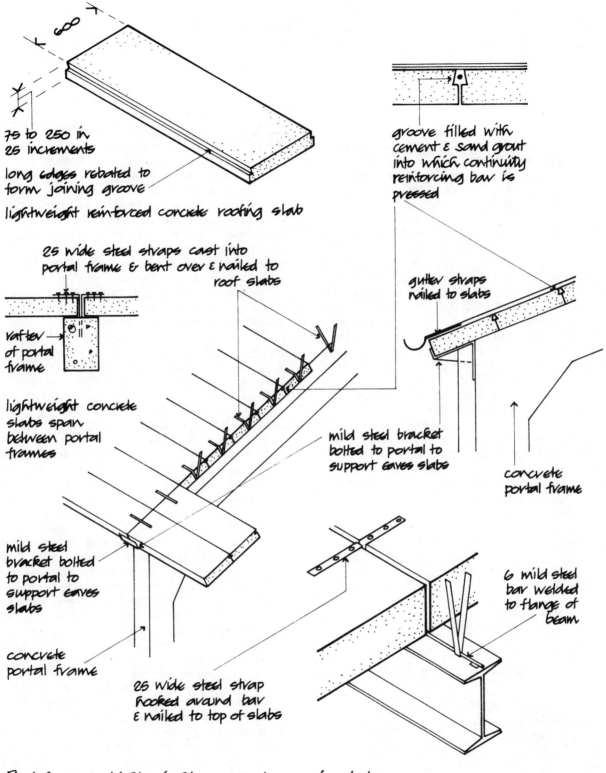

75 to 250 in 25 increments

long edges rebated to form joining groove

lightweight reinforced concrete roofing slab

groove filled with cement & sand grout into which continuity reinforcing bar is pressed

25 wide steel straps cast into portal frame & bent over & nailed to roof slabs

rafter of portal frame

gutter straps nailed to slabs

lightweight concrete slabs span between portal frames

mild steel bracket bolted to portal to support eaves slabs

concrete portal frame

mild steel bracket bolted to portal to support eaves slabs

concrete portal frame

6 mild steel bar welded to flange of beam

25 wide steel strap hooked around bar & nailed to top of slabs

Reinforced lightweight concrete roof slabs

Fig. 70

47

CHAPTER THREE

ROOFLIGHTS

The useful penetration of daylight through windows in the walls of buildings is some 6.0 to 9.0 inside the building, depending on the level of the head of windows above floor level. It is plain, therefore, that inside a building in excess of 12.0 to 18.0 in width or length there will be areas to which a useful degree of daylight will not penetrate through windows in walls.

The traditional means of providing daylight penetration to the working surfaces of large single-storey buildings is through roof lights either fixed in the slope of roofs or as upstand lights in flat roofs. Usual practice was to cover the middle third of each slope of symmetrical pitch roofs and the whole of north facing slopes of north light roofs with rooflights and about a third of the area of flat roofs with upstand rooflights. The penetration of daylight through these rooflights provided adequate natural light on working surfaces in factories and workshops for bench level, hand operated activities.

With the very considerable increase in automated processes of manufacturing not dependent on bench level, hand controlled operations, the provision of natural daylighting through roofs is often a disadvantage due to the variability of natural daylight and shadows cast by heavy overhead moving machinery, to the extent that artificial illumination by itself has become common in many modern factories and workshops.

The advantage of economy and convenience in the use of natural lighting from rooflights has to be balanced against the disadvantages of the poor thermal and sound insulation, discomfort from glare, solar heat gain and the hazards of fire from the materials used for rooflights.

Functional requirements

The primary function of rooflights is:

Admission of daylight.

The functional requirements of rooflights as a component part of roofs are:

Strength and stiffness
Exclusion of wind and rain
Thermal insulation
Sound insulation
Fire resistance and safety from fire.

Daylight

The prime function of rooflights is to admit an adequate quantity of daylight with minimum diversity and without excessive direct view of the sky or penetration of direct sunlight. The area of the rooflights chosen for single-storey buildings is a compromise between the provision of adequate daylight and the need to limit loss of heat through the lights. The ratio of the area of rooflights to floor area is usually about 1 to 5 for most factory buildings with pitched roofs and about 1 to 3 for roofs with vertical monitor rooflights.

The quantity of daylight that is admitted through a window or rooflight is expressed as a daylight factor. The daylight factor is defined as the ratio of the daylight illumination at a point on a plane due to the light received directly or indirectly from a sky of assumed or known luminance distribution, to the illuminance on a horizontal plane due to an unobtrusive hemisphere of this sky.

It has been practice for some time to determine the required area of window or rooflight from the minimum daylight factor, which is the daylight at the worst-lit point on the working plane assuming that if there is adequate daylight at the worst-lit point there will be adequate light at all other points. This assumption is reasonable where specific critical judgements in daylight alone, which depend on colour, contrast and detail, such as clinical judgements in a hospital, have to be made. Even though daylight at the worst-lit point may be satisfactory for a specific task, the daylight in the room or area as a whole may not be entirely satisfactory. The minimum daylight factor, in current use, which gives an indication of daylight requirements at a given point for the performance of critical tasks, does not provide a wholly satisfactory indication of the distribution of light in a particular room or area for a variety of activities.

In DD73. 1982, which is a draft for development as a preliminary to the publication of a new Code for Daylighting, it is proposed that an average daylight factor and the uniformity ratio be adopted as a better indication of the daylight requirements more closely matching the specific requirements of distribution of illuminance and luminance in a specific room than that given by a minimum daylight factor alone. It is likely that this proposal will be accepted for inclusion in a new Code for Daylighting.

The average daylight factor may be calculated from the formula:

average daylight factor =

$$\frac{\text{Total incident light flux on working plane}}{\text{outdoor illuminance} \times \text{area of working plane}}$$

The uniformity ratio, which is an indication of the diversity of daylight, is the ratio of

$$\frac{\text{minimum daylight factor}}{\text{average daylight factor}}$$

The lower the uniformity ratio, the greater the diversity of illuminance, and the higher the uniformity ratio, the better the lighting.

The recommendations for average daylight factors and minimum uniformity ratios of daylight for working places given in DD 73.1982 are:

Type of day-light	Average daylight factor on reference plane	Uniformity ratio	
		Top lit	Side lit
Full daylight	5	0.7	0.3
Supplemented daylight	2	0.7	0.3

Glare, discomfort and disability: Glare is the word used to describe the effect of excessive contrast, in a fixed direction of view, between a very bright light source and a relatively dark background light, such as the contrast of a window at the end of a dark corridor, which may cause discomfort without reducing vision, or the contrast of a very bright skylight at the top of a stair which can cause disability to vision.

Both discomfort and disability glare are caused by excessive contrast and unfavourable distribution of luminance in the visual field. Discomfort glare, which is directly related to the absolute luminance irrespective of whether there is unfavourable contrast present, may occur on a bright day in a room that is comfortable on a dull day.

The discomfort glare index is an expression of subjective discomfort in relation to the luminance of windows, average luminance of interiors and the direction of the source of glare, related to the normal direction of viewing. A table of glare constants is set out in DD 73.1982 to limit the degree of discomfort due to glare which is generally acceptable to occupants of rooms.

Rooflights should be of sufficient area to provide satisfactory daylight and be spaced to give reasonable uniformity of lighting on the working surface without excessive direct view of the sky, to minimise glare or penetration of direct sunlight and to avoid excessive solar heat gain.

In pitched roofs, rooflights are usually formed in the slopes of the roof to give an area of glass of about one fifth of the floor area and spaced as indicated in Fig. 71 to give good uniformity and distribution of light. Rooflights in flat roofs are constructed with upstand curbs to provide an upstand to which the roof covering can be finished. The area of the lights should be about one fifth of the floor area and spaced similar to lights in pitched roofs. Monitor rooflights with either vertical or sloping lights give reasonable uniformity and distribution of light with the spacing shown in Fig. 71. Vertical monitor lights should have a glazed area of about a third of the floor area to provide adequate daylight to the working plane. North light roofs, with the whole or a large part of the north facing slopes glazed, are adopted to avoid or minimise sun glare and solar heat gain. In consequence the daylight is from one direction with less uniformity of distribution and stronger modelling than with lights in symmetrical pitch or flat roofs. The area of glazing of north lights should be about one third of the floor area and the spacing of the lights is shown in Fig. 71.

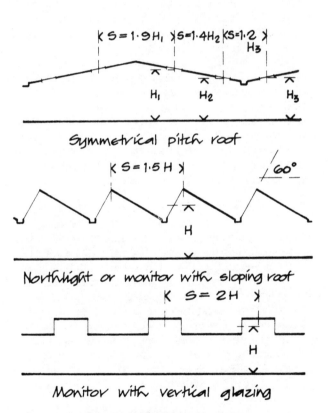

Symmetrical pitch roof

Northlight or monitor with sloping roof

Monitor with vertical glazing

Spacing of rooflights
Fig. 71

Strength and stiffness: The materials used for rooflights, glass and flat or profiled, transparent or translucent sheets, are used in the form of thin sheets to obtain maximum transmission of light and for economy. Glass which has poor tensile strength requires support at the comparatively close centres of about 600 to provide adequate strength and stiffness as part of the roof covering. Plastic sheets that are profiled to match sheet metal and asbestos cement roof coverings, for the sake of weathering at end and side laps, have adequate strength in the material of the sheets and stiffness in the depth of the profile for the comparatively wide centres normal to pitched roof coverings. Plastic sheets which are extruded in the form of double or treble skin cellular flat sheets have good strength and stiffness in the nature of the material and the cellular form in which they are used.

Exclusion of wind and rain: The metal glazing bars used to provide support for glass are made with either non-ferrous flashings or plastic cappings and gaskets that fit over the glass to exclude wind and rain together with top and bottom non-ferrous metal flashings to overlap and underlap profiled sheet coverings pitched at least 15 degrees to the horizontal.

Profiled plastic sheets fixed in the slope of pitched roofs are designed to provide an adequate side lap and sufficient end lap to give the same resistance to the penetration of wind and rain as the profiled metal or asbestos cement in which they are fixed at a pitch or slope of not less than 10 degrees to the horizontal.

Cellular flat plastic sheets are fitted with metal or plastic gaskets to weather the joints between the sheets fixed down the slope of roofs and non-ferrous metal flashings at overlaps at the top and bottom of sheets.

Rooflights in flat roofs and low pitch roofs are fixed on a curb to which an upstand skirting of the roof covering is dressed to exclude rain with the rooflight overlapping the curb to exclude rain and with wind stops as necessary between the light and the curb.

Thermal insulation: Because the thin sheets of glass or plastic used for rooflights offer little resistance to the transfer of heat, the area of rooflights is limited to that necessary to provide sufficient daylight. Some reduction in transfer of heat is effected by the use of double glazing in the form of two skins of glass or plastic sheeting and the double or triple skin, cellular flat sheets of plastic. It is plainly impractical to clean the surfaces of glass or plastic sheets inside the air space of double glazing which will in time suffer a reduction in light transmission due to accumulations of dust and condensation on surfaces inside the air space. Sealed double glazing units of glass or plastic sheets will prevent this loss of light transmission.

Sound insulation: The thin sheets of glass and plastic used for rooflights offer little resistance to the transfer of sound. Double skin glass and plastic sheets will effect some little reduction in transfer of sound. Where sound reduction is a critical requirement of a roof it is necessary to use the mass of a material such as concrete for the roof without any rooflights or with concrete lens lights.

Fire resistance and safety from fire: This is the functional requirement of roofs that is the principal limitation to the use of rooflights. The thin sheet materials used for rooflights have poor resistance to damage by the heat generated in fires as glass shatters and plastics melt, and in consequence the lights offer poor resistance to the spread of fire between adjacent parts of buildings and between adjacent buildings.

Materials used for rooflights
Glass: This is the traditional material for rooflights, used in the form of flat sheets supported by metal glazing bars fixed in the slope of the roofs of buildings, used as flat sheets fixed in metal frames for deck and lantern lights, and shaped for use as domelights.

The types of glass used for rooflights today are float glass (see Volume 2) that is transparent and has flat, parallel, bright, fire-polished surfaces with no distortion, solar control glass to limit the admission of solar radiation, patterned glass which is textured or patterned and is translucent, and wired glass which is used to minimise the danger from broken glass during fires.

Glass has poor mechanical strength and requires the support of metal glazing bars at comparatively close centres of about 600 for use as patent glazing in the slope of roofs and as side wall glazing. The need for glazing bars to provide support for glass and the necessary flashings or caps and gaskets for weathering adds considerably to the cost of glass for rooflights.

Glass affords little resistance to the transfer of heat, the U value of single glazing being 5.7 W/m^2°C for 6 glass. A comparatively small increase in the resistance to transfer of heat is effected by the use of double glazing, the U value of typical double glazing being 2.8 W/m^2°C.

The thin solid material of glass offers poor resistance to the transfer of sound.

When subjected to the heat generated by fires in buildings ordinary glass quickly cracks, falls away from its support and presents a hazard to those below, and it is a poor barrier to the spread of fire within and between buildings. The wire mesh that is embedded in wired glass will hold together glass that cracks when subjected to the heat of fires and so minimises the danger from broken glass and will also maintain the glass as a barrier to the spread of fire for a period of from half to one hour. For this reason wired glass is used for rooflights.

The principal advantage of glass is that as it is transparent it provides a clear undistorted view and also because it has a bright, fire-glazed finish it is easily cleaned by washing and maintains its clear lustrous finish without discolouring or yellowing with age. Glass is still used considerably for roof and wall lights in the form of patent glazing for the sake of a clear view and its lustrous finish, as compared to the translucent, dull opaque finish of the cheaper material, plastic.

Profiled, cellular and flat plastic sheets: Plastic sheet material which is transparent or translucent and can be shaped to match the profiles of metal and asbestos cement sheeting is extensively used as rooflights in the slopes of pitched roofs.

The materials used for profiled sheets and domelights are:

UPVC – polyvinyl chloride – rigid PVC. This is the cheapest of the translucent plastic materials used for profiled sheeting for rooflights. It has reasonable light transmittance (77%), reasonable impact and scratch resistance, adequate strength for use as a profiled sheet for roofing and good resistance to damage in handling, fixing and use. It is resistant to attack from most chemicals and has a useful life of twenty years or more. On exposure to solar radiation the material discolours to the extent that there is an appreciable yellowing and reduction of light transmission after some ten years. Due to its low melting point, the material, when subjected to the temperatures generated by fires, melts but does not readily burn.

GRP – glass reinforced polyester. This has very good impact resistance, rigidity, dimensional stability and fairly good scratch resistance. The material is translucent and has moderate to reasonable light transmittance of from 50% to 70%. GRP has very good durability and resistance to damage in handling, fixing and use. When subjected to the temperatures generated by fires GRP is usually inflammable.

The plastic material used for flat sheets for rooflights is:

Polycarbonate – PC. This is extruded as flat, double and triple skin cellular sheets with good light transmittance (up to 88%), good resistance to weathering, reasonable durability and extremely good impact resistance. Polycarbonate is the most expensive of the plastic materials used for rooflights and is used principally for its impact resistance in situations where glass and other plastics would be damaged, and for the improved resistance to transfer of heat of the double and triple skin sheets.

Acrylic – polymethyl methacrylate – PMMA. This is used for shaped domelights. It has a hard smooth finish that is particularly free from dirt staining, excellent chemical resistance, good impact resistance and good resistance to ultra-violet radiation. The material melts and burns readily when subject to the heat generated by fires.

Rooflights in pitched roofs usually take the form of one or more continuous bays of glass or plastic sheets fixed in both slopes of symmetrical-pitch roofs, glass or plastic sheets to the whole or the major part of north facing slopes of north light roofs or upstand monitor rooflights fixed across the slopes of symmetrical-pitch roofs as illustrated in Fig. 72.

The most straightforward way of constructing rooflights in pitched roofs is by the use of sheets of uPVC or GRP formed to match the profile of the metal or asbestos cement sheet covering of the roof.

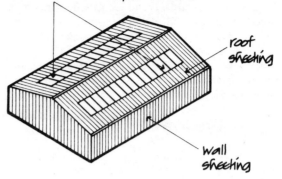

glazing or translucent sheeting to middle third of both slopes of roof

roof sheeting

wall sheeting

Roof lighting to symmetrical pitch roof

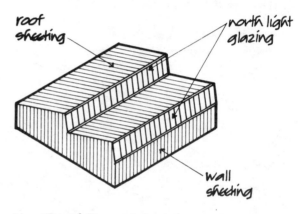

roof sheeting

north light glazing

wall sheeting

North light roof glazing

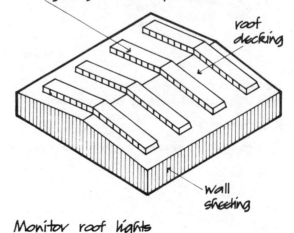

monitor roof lights between portal frames with glazing to both upstands

roof decking

wall sheeting

Monitor roof lights

Fig. 72

Translucent glass-reinforced polyester sheets composed of thermosetting polyester resins, curing agents, light stabilisers, flame retardants and reinforcing glass fibres are produced in a range of profiles to match most profiled metal and asbestos cement sheets. The light transmission of the clear sheets is 70%. Three grades of GRP sheet are produced to satisfy the conditions for external fire exposure and surface spread of flames set out in The Building Regulations 1976. The material has good strength and stability, is light-weight and shatterproof and has a life expectancy of twenty to thirty years. The sheets offer poor resistance to the transfer of heat, single skin sheets having a U value of 5.7 W/m^2 $^\circ$C, and double skin sheets, 2.8 W/m^2 $^\circ$C.

The sheets are laid to match the abutting metal or asbestos cement roof cladding sheets with side laps of corrugations or ridges to adjacent sheets and under and over end laps to match those of the roof sheeting. Sheets with

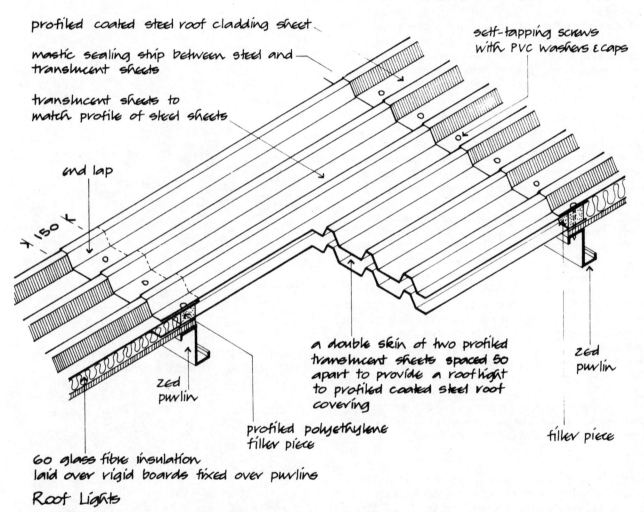

profiled coated steel roof cladding sheet

mastic sealing strip between steel and translucent sheets

translucent sheets to match profile of steel sheets

end lap

150

self-tapping screws with PVC washers & caps

a double skin of two profiled translucent sheets spaced 50 apart to provide a rooflight to profiled coated steel roof covering

zed purlin

zed purlin

profiled polyethylene filler piece

filler piece

60 glass fibre insulation laid over rigid boards fixed over purlins

Roof Lights

Translucent sheets in profiled steel covered pitched roof

Fig. 73

52

a profile that is less than 35 deep should not be used on a roof pitched at less than 10 degrees and those with profiles 35 or more deep can be laid on roofs pitched as low as 4 degrees to the horizontal provided all laps are sealed. Where GRP sheets overlap one another and where GRP sheets overlap metal or asbestos cement sheets on roofs pitched below 20 degrees, all side and end laps must be sealed with self-adhesive closed cell PVC sealing tape to make a weathertight joint.

In common with other lightweight sheeting material used for roofing, the fixing of these sheets is critical to

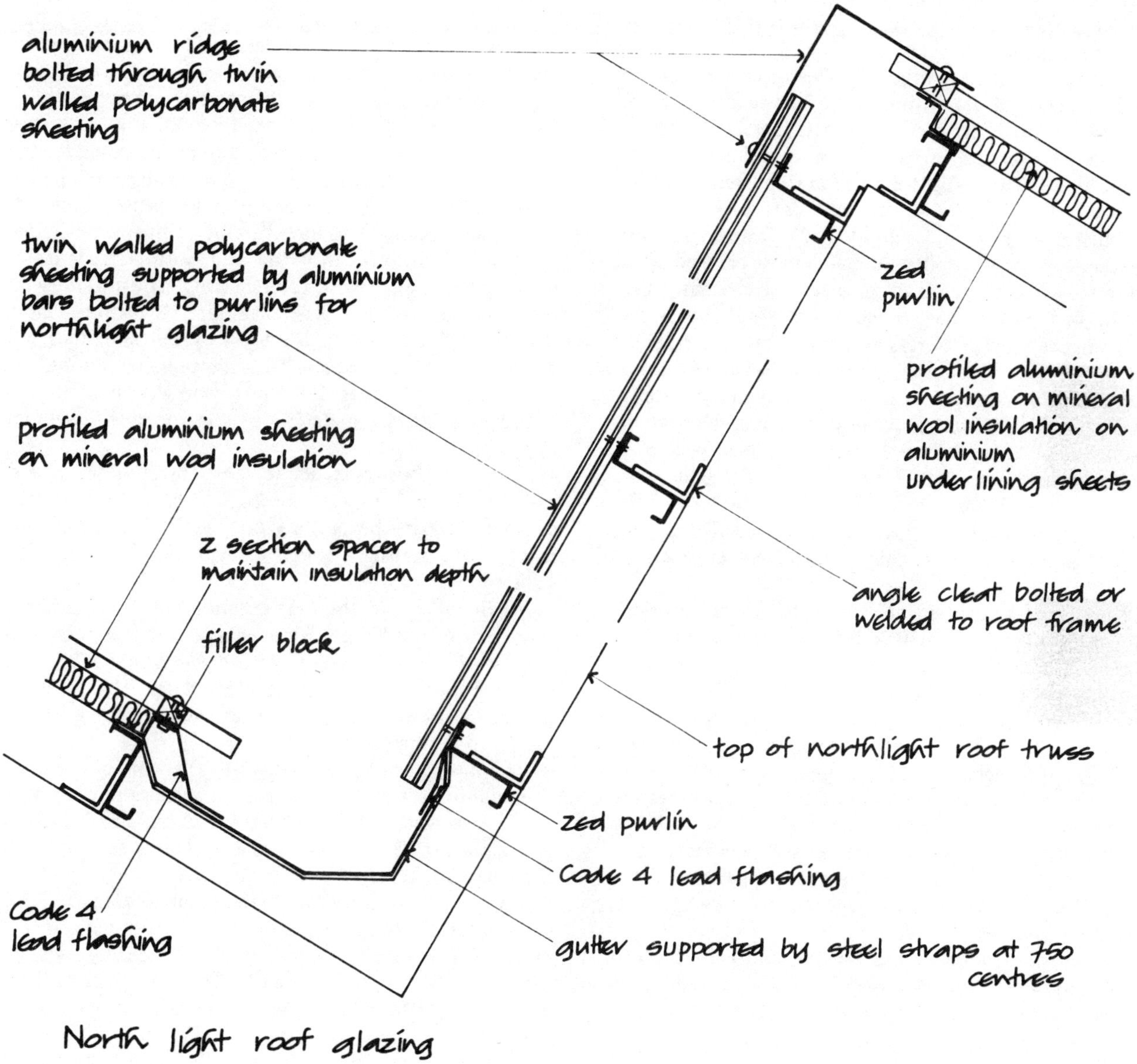

aluminium ridge bolted through twin walled polycarbonate sheeting

twin walled polycarbonate sheeting supported by aluminium bars bolted to purlins for northlight glazing

profiled aluminium sheeting on mineral wool insulation

z section spacer to maintain insulation depth

filler block

Code 4 lead flashing

zed purlin

profiled aluminium sheeting on mineral wool insulation on aluminium underlining sheets

angle cleat bolted or welded to roof frame

top of northlight roof truss

zed purlin

Code 4 lead flashing

gutter supported by steel straps at 750 centres

North light roof glazing

Fig. 74

53

resist uplift from wind suction which dictates the necessary centres for the fixing of fasteners. The sheets are fixed with the same type of fasteners that are used for metal or asbestos cement sheeting, self-drilling and self-tapping or self-tapping for metal sheets to metal purlins, and hook bolts to hot rolled steel purlins being used with PVC washers and neoprene gaskets to make a watertight seal.

Double skin rooflights are constructed with two skins of GRP as illustrated in Fig. 73, with two sheets of the same profile as the metal sheet roof covering or two sheets of GRP to match the profiles of asbestos cement roofing and underlining sheets, with polyethylene spacers to maintain the air space between the sheets. Sealing strips are fixed at all overlaps to exclude wind and rain. Sealed double skin GRP rooflight units are made from a profiled top sheet which is sealed to a flat undersheet.

Transparent polyvinyl chloride (uPVC) sheets are produced in a range of profiles to match most profiled metal and asbestos cement cladding sheets. The light transmission of the clear sheet is about 80%. The material has good impact resistance, reasonable strength and stability and is light-weight and shatterproof. It has a life expectancy of up to ten years because, even though the material is UV stabilised, it will gradually discolour and lose transparency to an appreciable extent. The sheets provide poor thermal insulation, the U value of single skin being 5.7 $W/m^2 {}^\circ C$ and double skin 2.8 $W/m^2 {}^\circ C$. Because of the low melting point of the material, uPVC sheets melt but do not readily burn when subjected to the heat generated by fires.

These sheets are laid to match metal and asbestos cement roofing sheets with side laps of corrugations or ridges and under and over end laps to match the laps for abutting roof sheeting. For roof pitches of 15 degrees and less all laps over or under metal and asbestos cement sheets should be sealed with sealing strips and all laps between uPVC sheets should be sealed.

Uplift due to wind suction dictates the necessary centres of fixing for fasteners that should be fitted to holes in the sheets that are 3 larger than the fastener to allow for the considerable thermal expansion of the material. Fasteners similar to those used for roofing sheets are used to fix these sheets.

Double skin rooflights are formed with two sheets of profiled uPVC with plastic spacers or as sealed double skin rooflights with a profiled top sheet and a flat under sheet.

Transparent double or triple skin cellular flat sheets of polycarbonate are used for rooflights because of the extremely good impact resistance of the material. The light transmission of the single clear sheet is about 80%. Because of the cellular structure these flat sheets have good strength and stability and a U value for the double skin sheet of 2.8 $W/m^2 {}^\circ C$. In common with other plastic materials polycarbonate melts when subjected to the heat generated by fires. Polycarbonate sheeting is more expensive than either uPVC or GRP.

The flat cellular sheets of polycarbonate are supported by aluminium glazing bars fixed to purlins. The capping of the glazing bars compresses a neoprene gasket to the sheets to make a weathertight seal. Fig. 74 is an illustration of polycarbonate sheeting used as rooflight to the north facing slope of a north light roof.

Patent glazing

The traditional method of fixing glass in the slopes of roofs as rooflights is by means of wood or metal glazing bars that provide support for the glass and form weather flashings or cappings to exclude rain. The word 'patent' refers to the patents taken out by the original makers of glazing bars for rooflights. The original wood, iron and steel glazing bars have been replaced by aluminium and lead or plastic coated steel bars. The disadvantage of patent glazing is the considerable labour and expense in the provision and fixing of glazing bars at comparatively close centres and the necessary top and bottom flashings to weather the overlap with roof sheeting. The advantage of patent glazing is that glass maintains its lustrous, hard, fire-glazed finish which is easy to clean and does not discolour, and so reduce light transmission during the useful life of buildings. For this reason glass is often preferred as a glazing material for the roofs and walls of buildings.

Glass has poor resistance to the transfer of heat, the U value of single 6 thick glass being 5.7 $W/m^2 {}^\circ C$, and that of double glazing being 2.8 $W/m^2 {}^\circ C$. Glass is a comparatively heavy glazing material being 15 kg/m^2 for 6 thick glass.

When subject to the heat generated by fires, ordinary glass shatters and falls. Wired glass is used in rooflights because the wire embedded in the glass keeps it in place for some time once the glass shatters in heat, thus reducing the hazard from falling glass and maintaining the glass as a barrier to the spread of fire.

The most commonly used glazing bars are of extruded aluminium with seatings for glass, condensation channels and a deep web with top flange for strength and stiffness in supporting the weight of glass. Glass is secured with clips, beads or screwed or snap-on cappings.

Fig. 75 is an illustration of aluminium glazing bars used to support single sheet wired glass as rooflights in the slope of a symmetrical-pitch roof. The glazing bars are secured in fixing shoes screwed or bolted to angles fixed to purlins and fitted with aluminium stops to prevent the glass slipping down the slope of the roof. Aluminium spring clips, fitted to grooves in the bars, keep the glass in place and serve as weathering between the glass and the bar.

A system of steel battens and angles and an angle and a purlin provide a fixing for glass and sheeting at the overlap of the rooflight and the sheeting as illustrated in Fig. 75. Lead flashings are fixed as weathering at the overlaps of glass and sheeting.

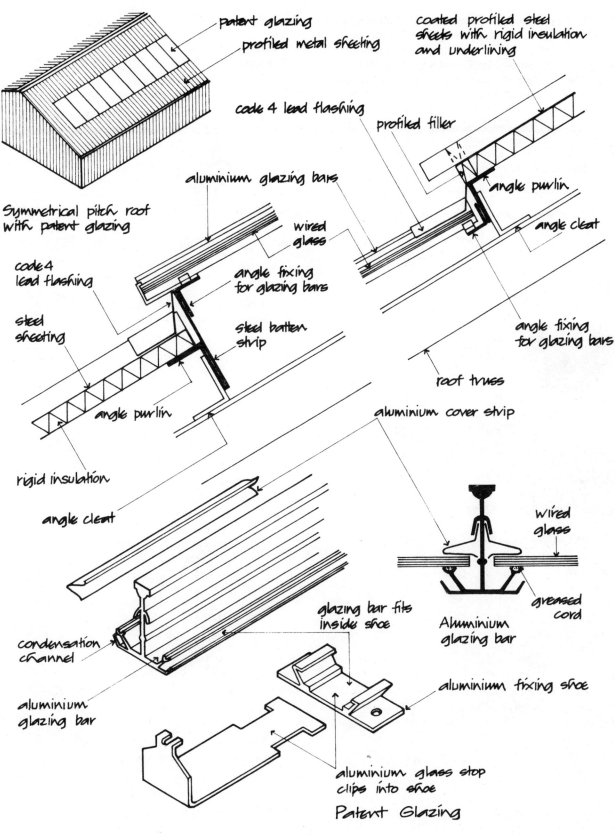

patent glazing

profiled metal sheeting

coated profiled steel sheets with rigid insulation and underlining

code 4 lead flashing

profiled filler

aluminium glazing bars

wired glass

angle purlin

angle cleat

Symmetrical pitch roof with patent glazing

code 4 lead flashing

steel sheeting

angle fixing for glazing bars

steel batten strip

angle fixing for glazing bars

angle purlin

roof truss

rigid insulation

aluminium cover strip

angle cleat

wired glass

condensation channel

glazing bar fits inside shoe

Aluminium glazing bar

greased cord

aluminium glazing bar

aluminium fixing shoe

aluminium glass stop clips into shoe

Patent Glazing

Fig. 75

55

Fig. 76 is an illustration of an aluminium glazing bar for single glazing and an aluminium glazing bar for sealed double glazing units that are secured with aluminium beads bolted to the bar and weathered with butyl strips.

Figs 77 and 78 are illustrations of aluminium glazing bars with bolted aluminium capping and snap-on aluminium capping to the bars. Cappings are used to secure glass in position on steep slopes and for vertical glazing as they afford a more secure fixing than spring clips and also for appearance sake to give more emphasis to the bars which would otherwise look somewhat insignificant.

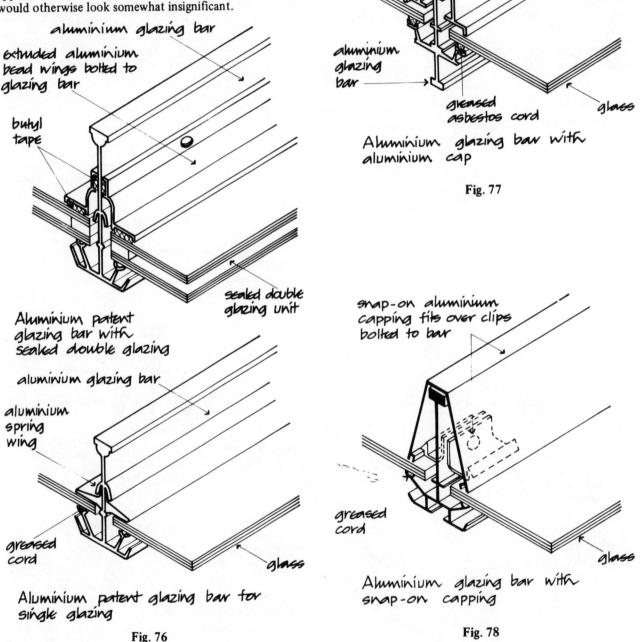

aluminium glazing bar

extruded aluminium bead wings bolted to glazing bar

butyl tape

sealed double glazing unit

Aluminium patent glazing bar with sealed double glazing

aluminium glazing bar

aluminium spring wing

greased cord

glass

Aluminium patent glazing bar for single glazing

Fig. 76

aluminium alloy cap bolted to bar

aluminium glazing bar

greased asbestos cord

glass

Aluminium glazing bar with aluminium cap

Fig. 77

snap-on aluminium capping fits over clips bolted to bar

greased cord

glass

Aluminium glazing bar with snap-on capping

Fig. 78

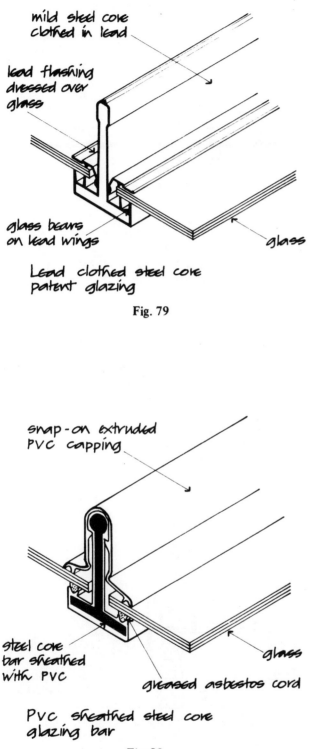

mild steel core clothed in lead

lead flashing dressed over glass

glass bears on lead wings

glass

Lead clothed steel core patent glazing

Fig. 79

snap-on extruded PVC capping

steel core bar sheathed with PVC

greased asbestos cord

glass

PVC sheathed steel core glazing bar

Fig. 80

Figs 79 and 80 are illustrations of steel bars covered with lead and PVC sheathing as a protection against corrosion. Steel bars are used for the mechanical strength of the material and the advantage of more widely spaced supports than is possible with aluminium bars of similar section.

Rooflights in flat and low pitch roofs

Before the introduction of plastic and fibre glass as materials for rooflights, the majority of rooflights to flat roofs were constructed as lantern lights or deck lights which were framed in timber or steel and covered with glass.

A lantern light is constructed with glazed vertical sides and a hipped or gable ended glazed roof. The vertical sides of the lantern light are used as opening lights for ventilation, as illustrated in Fig. 81. Lantern lights were often used to cover considerable areas, the light being framed with substantial timbers or iron or steel frames in the form of a glazed roof to provide top light to large stair wells and large internal rooms. The traditional lantern light of timber or steel requires frequent and careful maintenance if it is to remain sound and watertight. Lantern lights have largely been replaced by plastic domelights for economy in first cost and freedom from maintenance. The advantage of the lantern light is the facility of ventilation from the opening upstand sides that can be controlled by cord or winding gear from below to suit the occupants of the room.

Fig. 82 is an illustration of an aluminium lantern light constructed with standard aluminium window frame and sash sections, aluminium corner posts and aluminium patent glazing to the pitched roof with an aluminium ridge section. The aluminium sections require no maintenance other than occasional washing. In common with all rooflights fixed in flat roofs, the lantern light illustrated in Fig. 82 is fixed to an upstand curb to which the upstand skirting of the roof covering is dressed.

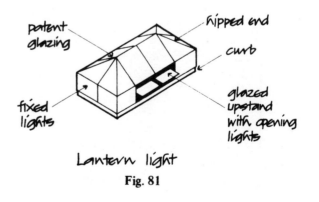

patent glazing

hipped end

curb

fixed lights

glazed upstand with opening lights

Lantern light

Fig. 81

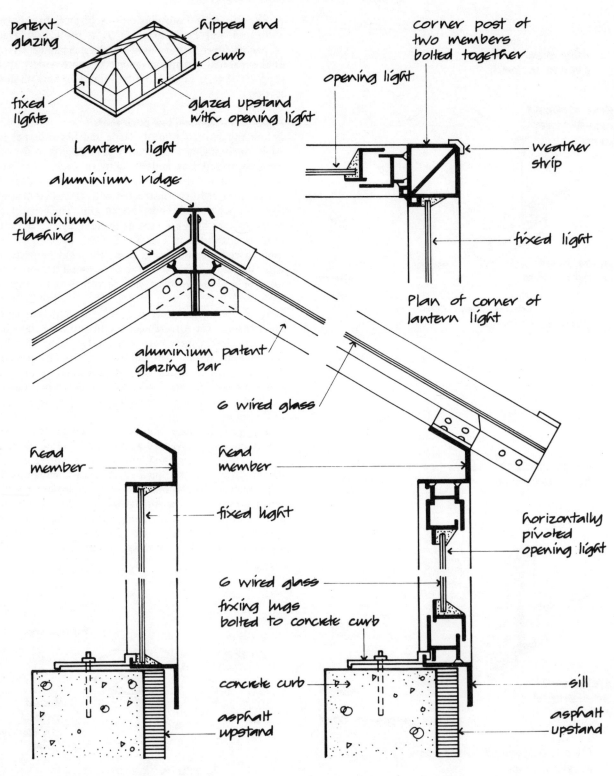

patent glazing

hipped end

curb

fixed lights

glazed upstand with opening light

Lantern light

corner post of two members bolted together

opening light

weather strip

fixed light

Plan of corner of lantern light

aluminium ridge

aluminium flashing

aluminium patent glazing bar

6 wired glass

head member

head member

fixed light

horizontally pivoted opening light

6 wired glass

fixing lugs bolted to concrete curb

concrete curb

sill

asphalt upstand

asphalt upstand

Aluminium lantern light

Fig. 82

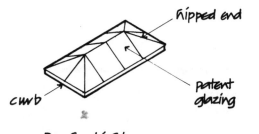

Deck light

Fig. 83

Deck lights are constructed as a hipped or gable ended glazed roof with no upstand sides. The deck light does not provide a means of ventilation and serves solely as a rooflight as shown in Fig. 83. The deck light illustrated in Fig. 84 in constructed with lead sheathed steel glazing bars pitched and fixed to a ridge and bolted to a steel tee fixed to the upstand curb.

The monopitch light, illustrated in Fig. 85, combines the simplicity of construction of a single slope for roof lighting with the advantage of one glazed upstand side for ventilation from one direction.

The nature of the materials, glass, reinforced plastic,

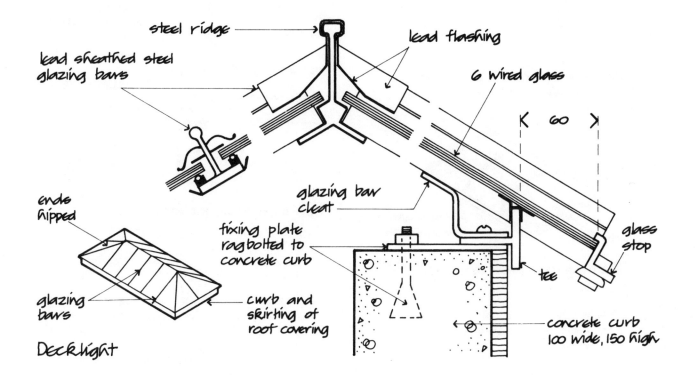

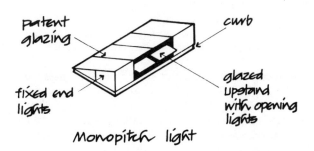

Decklight

Fig. 84

patent glazing

curb

fixed end lights

glazed upstand with opening lights

Monopitch light

Fig. 85

uPVC, acrylic and polycarbonate, facilitates the production of a range of shaped rooflights for use in flat and low-pitch roofs. The disadvantage of these materials is that they discolour and may require replacement after some ten years to restore daylight penetration.

One of the most commonly used rooflights in use to-day for flat roofs is the square-base dome light illustrated in Fig. 86. These lights can be formed in one piece to cover small openings or made up in sections and joined with glazing bars to provide a rooflight through large openings. The advantage of this type of rooflight is that it is economical to manufacture and fix, is light-weight and has adequate strength and stiffness from the curved shape of the light.

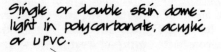

Single or double skin domelight in polycarbonate, acrylic
or UPVC.

curb

Domelight

rectangular base single or double
skin domelight in polycarbonate,
acrylic or UPVC.

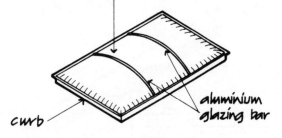

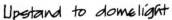

aluminium
glazing bar

curb

Rectangular base domelight

Single or double skin pyramid
roof light in polycarbonate acrylic
or UPVC.

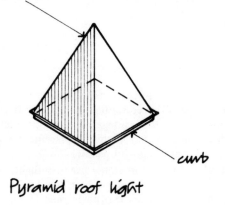

curb

Pyramid roof light

Fig. 86

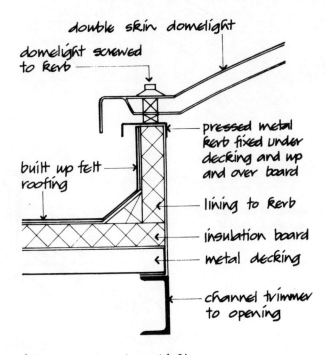

double skin domelight

domelight screwed
to kerb

built up felt
roofing

pressed metal
kerb fixed under
decking and up
and over board

lining to kerb

insulation board

metal decking

channel trimmer
to opening

Upstand to domelight

Fig. 87

The round-base dome light, shown in Fig. 86, is more expensive to construct than the square-base dome light because of the additional labour and materials involved in trimming a round opening in roof constructions.

The pyramid light, illustrated in Fig. 86, is used for appearance sake as the steeply sloping sides afford no increase in light penetration through the opening in the roof.

Plastic rooflights are made as either single skin lights or as sealed double skin lights which improves their resistance to transfer of heat.

Plastic rooflights are bolted or screwed to upstand curbs formed on the roof to which an upstand skirting of the roof covering is dressed as illustrated in Fig. 87.

Lens lights: These consist of square or round glass blocks or lenses that are cast into reinforced concrete ribs, as illustrated in Fig. 88, to provide diffused daylight through concrete roofs. The lens light can be pre-cast and bedded in place on site or in-situ cast in a concrete roof. The daylight transmission of these lights is poor as compared to other forms of rooflight. Lens lights are used in concrete roofs as rooflights to provide resistance to fire and also for reasons of security.

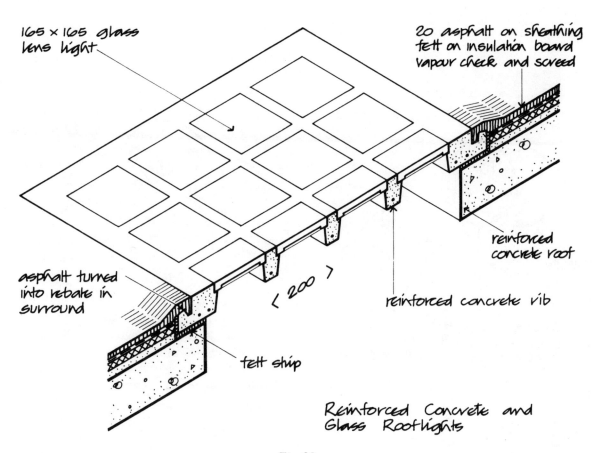

165 × 165 glass lens light

20 asphalt on sheathing felt on insulation board vapour check and screed

reinforced concrete roof

asphalt turned into rebate in surround

< 200 >

reinforced concrete rib

felt strip

Reinforced Concrete and Glass Rooflights

Fig. 88

CHAPTER FOUR

SHELL STRUCTURES

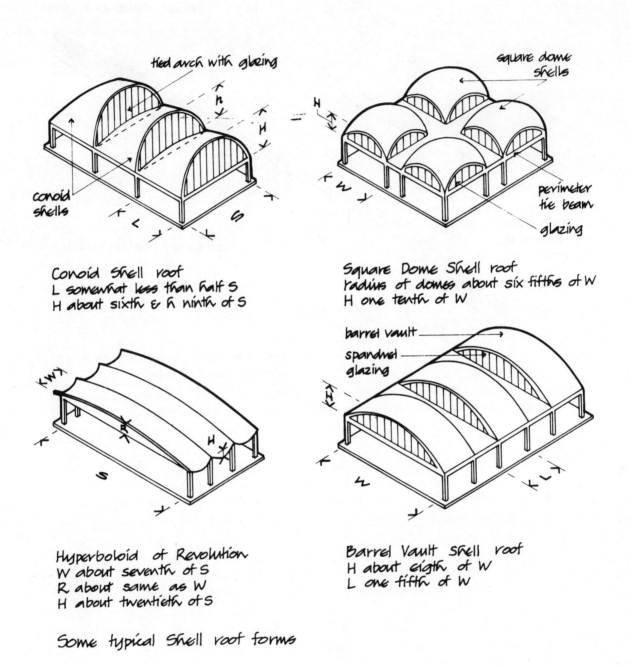

tied arch with glazing

conoid shells

square dome shells

perimeter tie beam

glazing

Conoid Shell roof
L somewhat less than half S
H about sixth & h ninth of S

Square Dome Shell roof
radius of domes about six fifths of W
H one tenth of W

barrel vault
spandrel glazing

Hyperboloid of Revolution
W about seventh of S
R about same as W
H about twentieth of S

Barrel Vault Shell roof
H about eigth of W
L one fifth of W

Some typical Shell roof forms

Fig. 89

Lattice and portal frame buildings consist of a structural frame which supports sheet or slab roof and wall covering. The frames serve purely as a structural support for the roof and wall covering that encloses the building and provides protection against weather. The roof and wall covering add nothing to the strength and rigidity of the structural frame.

A shell structure is a thin, curved membrane or slab, usually of reinforced concrete, that functions both as structure and covering, the structure deriving its strength and rigidity from the curved shell form. The term shell is used to describe these structures by reference to the very considerable strength and rigidity of thin, natural, curved forms such as the shell of an egg, a nut and crustaceans such as the tortoise. The strength and rigidity of curved shell structures makes it possible to construct single curved barrel vaults 60 thick and double curved hyperbolic paraboloids 40 thick in reinforced concrete for spans of 30.0.

Shell structures are sometimes described as single or double curvature shells. Single curvature shells, curved on one linear axis, are part of a cylinder or cone in the form of barrel vaults and conoid shells, as illustrated in Fig. 89. Double curvature shells are either part of a sphere, as a dome, or a hyperboloid of revolution, as illustrated in Fig. 89. The terms single curvature and double curvature do not provide a precise geometric distinction between the form of shell structures as a barrel vault is a single curvature shell but so is a dome. The terms single curvature and double curvature are used to differentiate the comparative rigidity of the two forms and the complexity of the centering necessary to construct the shell form. Double curvature of a shell adds considerably to its stiffness, resistance to deformation under load and reduction in the need for restraint against deformation.

Centering is the term used to describe the necessary temporary support on which a curved reinforced concrete shell structure is cast. The centering for a single curvature barrel vault is less complex than that for a dome which is curved from a centre point.

The most straightforward shell construction is the barrel vault, which is part of a cylinder or barrel with the same curvature along its length, as shown in Fig. 90. The short-span barrel vault, illustrated in Fig. 90, is used for the width of the arch ribs between which the barrel vaults span. It is cast on similar arch ribs supporting straight timber or metal centering which is comparatively simple and economic to erect and which can, without waste, be taken down and used again for similar vaults. The centering for the conoid, dome and hyperboloid of revolution shells, illustrated in Fig. 89, is considerably more complex and therefore more expensive than that for a barrel vault because of the necessary additional labour and wasteful cutting of material to form support for shapes that are not of a linear uniform curvature.

The attraction of shell structures lies in the elegant simplicity of curved shell forms that utilise the natural strength and stiffness of shell forms with great economy in the use of material. The disadvantage of shell structures is their cost. A shell structure is many times more expensive than a portal framed structure covering the same floor area because of the considerable labour required to construct the centering on which the shell is cast.

The material most suited to the construction of a shell structure is concrete, which is a highly plastic material when first mixed with water that can take up any shape on centering or inside formwork. Small section reinforcing bars can readily be bent to follow the curvature of shells. Once the cement has set and the concrete hardened the reinforced concrete membrane or slab acts as a strong, rigid shell which serves as both structure and covering to the building.

Barrel vaults

Reinforced concrete barrel vaults: These consist of a thin membrane of reinforced concrete positively curved in one direction so that the vault acts as structure and roof surface. The concrete shell is from 57 to 75 thick for spans of 12.0 to 30.0 respectively. This thickness of concrete provides sufficient cover of concrete to protect the reinforcement against damage by fire and protection against

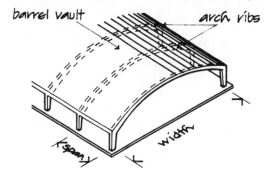

Short Span Barrel Vault

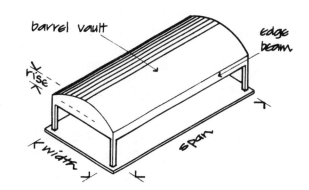

Long Span Barrel Vault

Fig. 90

corrosion. The wet concrete is spread over the centering around the reinforcement and compacted by hand to the required thickness. The stiffness of the concrete mix and the reinforcement prevent the concrete from running down the slope of the curvature of the shell while the concrete is wet.

The usual form of barrel vault is the long span vault illustrated in Fig. 90, where the strength and stiffness of the shell lies at right angles to the curvature so that the span is longitudinal to the curvature. The usual span of a long-span barrel vault is from 12.0 to 30.0, with the width being about half the span and the rise about one fifth of the width. To cover large areas, multi-span, multi-bay barrel vault roofs can be used where the roof is extended across the width of the vaults as a multi-bay roof as illustrated in Fig. 91, or as a multi-bay, multi-span roof as illustrated in Fig. 90.

Stiffening beams and arches: Under local loads the thin shell of the barrel vault will tend to distort and lose shape and if this distortion were of sufficient magnitude the resultant increase in local stress would cause the shell to progressively collapse. To strengthen the shell against this possibility, stiffening beams or arches are cast integrally with the shell.

Fig. 92 illustrates the four types of stiffening members generally used, common practice being to provide a stiffening member between the columns supporting the shell, that is at the limits of the span of the barrel vault. The downstand reinforced concrete beam, which is usually 150 or 225 thick, is the most efficient of the four because of its depth. To avoid the interruption of the line of the soffit of the vaults caused by a downstand beam, an upstand beam is sometimes used. The disadvantage of an upstand beam is that it breaks up the line of the roof and needs protection against weather.

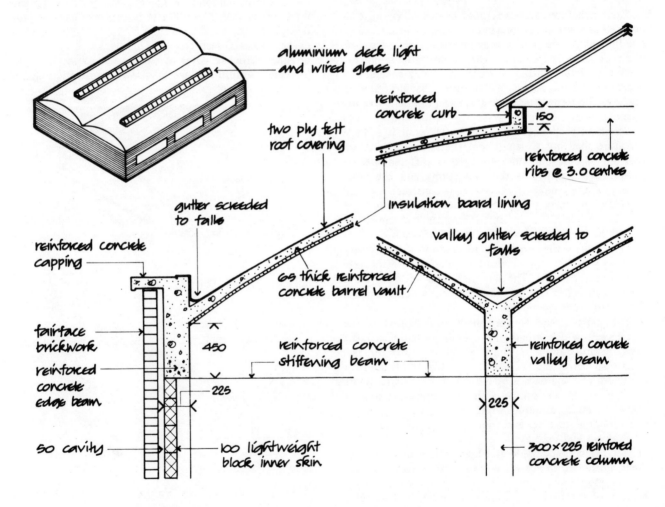

Reinforced concrete Barrel Vault.

Fig. 91

64

Arch ribs for stiffening barrel vaults, which are less efficient structurally because they usually have less depth than beams, are sometimes preferred for appearance sake as they follow the curve of the shell and therefore do not appear to interrupt the line of the vault as do beams. The spacing of arch ribs is the same as for beams.

Edge and valley beams: Due to self-weight and imposed loads the thin shell will tend to spread and its curvature flatten out. To resist this, reinforced concrete edge beams are cast between columns as an integral part of the shell. Edge beams may be cast as dropped beams or upstand beams or partly upstand and partly dropped beams, as illustrated in Fig. 93. The advantage of the dropped beam, illustrated in Fig. 90, is that it exposes the whole of the outside of the vault to view. This effect would be spoiled if a rain water gutter were to be fixed. In hot climates, where rain water rapidly evaporates and it is not practice to use gutters, the dropped beam edge finish is used. In temperate climates an upstand beam is usual to form a drainage channel for rain water (Fig. 91).

Similarly between multi-bay vaults a downstand or feather edge valley beam is cast as illustrated in Fig. 93. Spreading of the vaults is largely transmitted to adjacent shells and thence to edge beams on the boundary of roofs, so that comparatively slender feather edge or downstand valley beams are practical.

Rooflights: Top light through the barrel vault can be provided by deck lights formed in the crown of the vault, as illustrated in Fig. 91, or by dome lights. The deck light can be continuous along the crown or formed as individual lights. The rooflights are fixed to an upstand curb cast integrally with the shell as illustrated in Fig. 91. One of the advantages of these shells is that their concave soffit reflects and helps to disperse light over the area below. The disadvantage of these top lights is that they may cause overheating and glare in summer months.

Thermal insulation: The thin concrete shell offers poor resistance to transfer of heat so that some form of insulating soffit lining or a light-weight aggregate screed on the shell is necessary. The need to add some form of insulating lining to improve insulation adds considerably to the cost of the shell. Pliable insulating boards which can be laid on the centering and take up the curve of the vault will adhere sufficiently to the concrete of the shell to provide adequate fixing. The possibility of condensation forming on the underside of the cold concrete shell and so saturating the insulation make this an unsatisfactory finish to the soffit of the vault. To fix pre-formed insulating lining under the vault with a ventilated air space between the shell and the lining would be grossly expensive. The most satisfactory method of providing insulation is to spread a light-weight screed over the shell.

The difficulties of improving the insulation of shells, controlling condensation and at the same time maintaining the elegance of the curved shape of the shell makes these structures largely unsuited to heated buildings in temperate climates.

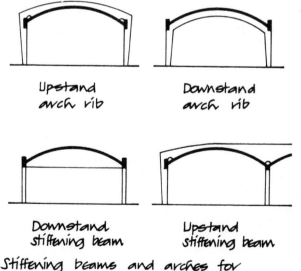

Stiffening beams and arches for reinforced concrete barrel vaults

Fig. 92

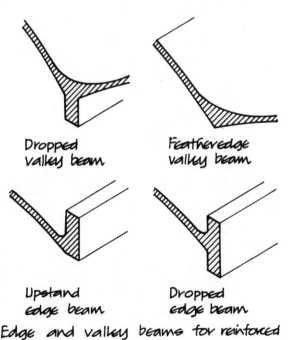

Edge and valley beams for reinforced concrete barrel vaults

Fig. 93

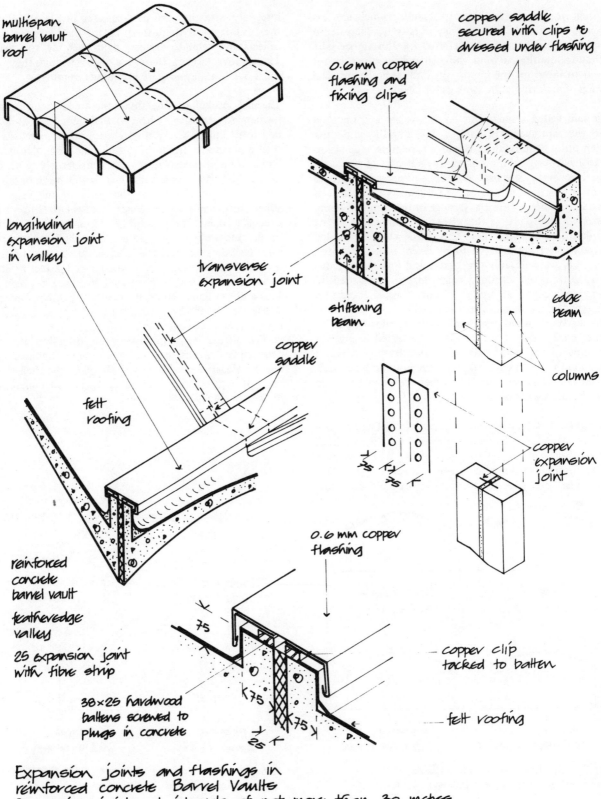

multispan barrel vault roof

longitudinal expansion joint in valley

transverse expansion joint

copper saddle

felt roofing

reinforced concrete barrel vault

feathevedge valley

25 expansion joint with fibre strip

38×25 hardwood battens screwed to plugs in concrete

0.6 mm copper flashing and fixing clips

copper saddle secured with clips to dressed under flashing

stiffening beam

edge beam

columns

copper expansion joint

0.6 mm copper flashing

copper clip tacked to batten

felt roofing

75

75

75

25

Expansion joints and flashings in reinforced concrete Barrel Vaults
Expansion joints at intervals of not more than 30 metres

Fig. 94

Expansion joints: With changes in temperature lineal expansion or contraction of these rigid concrete shells occurs. If there were excessive contraction or expansion the stresses so caused might deform the shell and cause gradual collapse. To limit expansion and contraction, continuous expansion joints are formed at intervals of about 30.0 both along the span and across the width of multibay, multi-span barrel vault roofs. In effect the expansion joint is formed by erecting separate shell structures each with its own supports and with compressible and expandable joint material between adjacent structures as illustrated in Fig. 94. The expansion joint transverse to the span of the vaults is formed by casting an upstand to adjacent stiffening beams with a non-ferrous flashing to weather the joint as shown in Fig. 94. The expansion joint is made continuous to the ground with double columns each side of a vertical expansion joint. Longitudinal expansion joints are formed in a valley with upstands weathered with non-ferrous capping over the joint (Fig. 94). This joint is continuous to the ground with a vertical expansion joint between a pair of columns.

Roof covering: Concrete shells may be covered with non-ferrous sheet metal, asphalt, bitumen felt, a plastic membrane or a liquid rubber based coating consisting of a neoprene (synthetic rubber) undercoat and chlorosulphonated polyethylene finishing coat applied by brush or spray with reinforcing tape bedded in the material over construction joints in the concrete. This elastomeric coating is supplied in six different colours and being extremely light in weight, that is 0.97 kg/m², and resilient is ideal as a covering for concrete shells. Built-up bituminous felt is often used because it is comparatively light in weight and cheap. Mastic asphalt roofing is a comparatively heavy covering (44 kg/m²) and is not much used for shell roofs. Non-ferrous sheet metal coverings are fixed to concrete shells in the same way that they are fixed to concrete roofs as described in Volume 1.

Walls: The walls of shell structures take the form of non-loadbearing panel walls of brick, block or timber built between or across columns to exclude wind and rain and as insulation against transfer of heat.

North light reinforced concrete barrel vault: To avoid the possibility of overheating and glare from toplights in the summer months a system of north light barrel vaults is used. The roof consists of a thin reinforced concrete shell on the south facing side of the roof, with a reinforced concrete framed north facing slope, pitched at from 60 to 80 degrees as illustrated in Fig. 95.

The rigidity of a barrel vault depends on its continuous curvature, which in this type of roof is interrupted by the north light opening. In consequence a north light shell is less efficient structurally than a barrel vault shell. The economic span of a north light shell is 12.0 to 15.0 as compared to the 30.0 or more of the barrel vault.

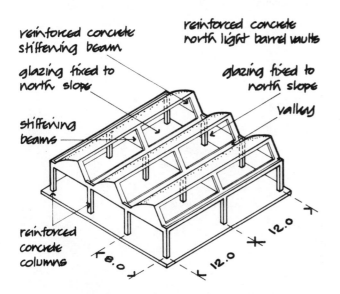

Three bay reinforced concrete north light Barrel Vault

Fig. 95

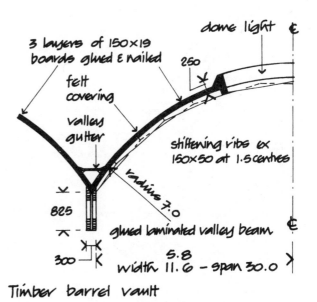

Timber barrel vault

Fig. 96

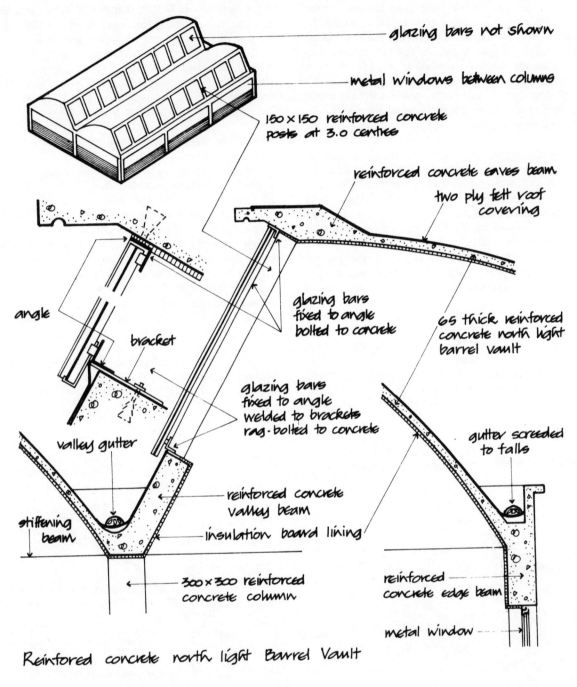

glazing bars not shown

metal windows between columns

150 × 150 reinforced concrete posts at 3.0 centres

reinforced concrete eaves beam

two ply felt roof covering

angle

bracket

glazing bars fixed to angle bolted to concrete

65 thick reinforced concrete north light barrel vault

glazing bars fixed to angle welded to brackets rag-bolted to concrete

valley gutter

gutter screeded to falls

stiffening beam

reinforced concrete valley beam

insulation board lining

300 × 300 reinforced concrete column

reinforced concrete edge beam

metal window

Reinforced concrete north light Barrel Vault

Fig. 97

The reinforced concrete beam and post framing in the north light slope serves as a deep open web beam supporting the crown of the vaulted slope. The north light framing may be open between supporting columns, as illustrated in Fig. 95, or stiffened with intermediate posts as illustrated in Fig. 97. Obviously an increase in the spacing of the posts of the north light frame will require an increase in the section of the eaves and valley beams shown in Fig. 97.

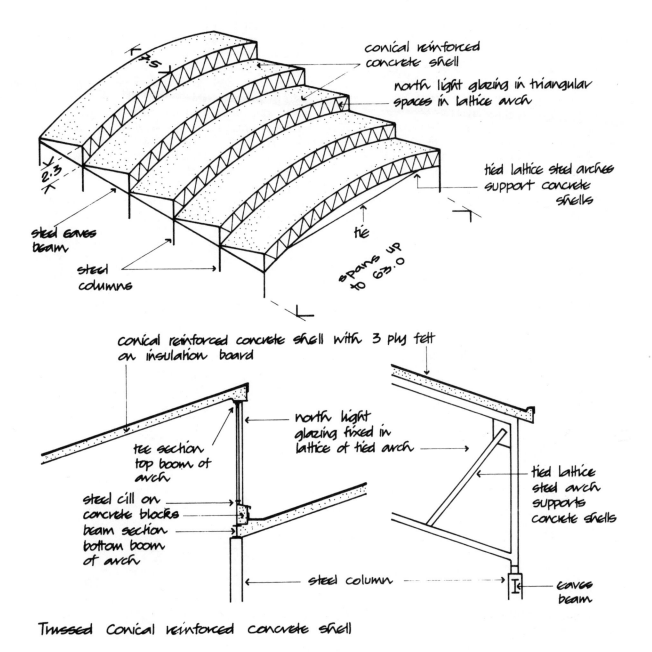

conical reinforced concrete shell

north light glazing in triangular spaces in lattice arch

tied lattice steel arches support concrete shells

tie

spans up to 0.69.0

steel eaves beam

steel columns

conical reinforced concrete shell with 3 ply felt on insulation board

north light glazing fixed in lattice of tied arch

tee section top boom of arch

steel cill on concrete blocks

beam section bottom boom of arch

tied lattice steel arch supports concrete shells

steel column

eaves beam

Trussed Conical reinforced concrete shell

Fig. 98

The description of stiffening beams and arches, edge beams, insulation, expansion joints and roof covering given under the heading of barrel vaults applies equally to north light vaults. The north light slope is glazed with patent metal glazing or profiled plastic sheeting fixed to timber grounds or metal angles screwed to the concrete as illustrated in Fig. 97.

Timber barrel vaults: Single and multi-bay barrel vaults can be constructed from small section timber with spans and widths similar to reinforced concrete barrel vaults. The vault is formed of three layers of boards glued and nailed together and stiffened with ribs at close centres, as shown in Fig. 96. The ribs serve both to stiffen the shell and to maintain the boards' curvature over the vault. Glued laminated edge and valley beams are formed to resist spreading of the vault.

There is no appreciable difference in cost between similar concrete and timber barrel vaults.

Reinforced concrete conoid shell roofs

In this shell form the curvature and rise of the shell increases from a shallow curve to a steeply curved end in which north light spandrel glazing is fixed as illustrated in Fig. 89. The glazed end of each shell consists of a reinforced concrete or steel lattice which serves as a stiffening beam to resist deformation of the shell. Edge beams resist spreading of the shell as previously described. ·

It will be seen from the illustration of this form in Fig. 89 that, because of the sharply curved glazed end, there is a considerable volume of space inside the shell which cannot be used for production or storage. This particular arrangement of conoid shells is not suitable for use over heated factories and warehouses but is used over long-span enclosures such as railway stations and covered markets where the enclosed space is not heated and a high roof is no disadvantage.

A system of in-situ or pre-cast unit concrete conoid shells with tied lattice steel arches in a range of standard sizes has been used with spans of up to 63.0 and in bays of 7.5, with north light glazing incorporated in the steel arch framing, as illustrated in Fig. 98. This roof system is reasonable in first cost, requires little maintenance and is suited to unheated long-span enclosures.

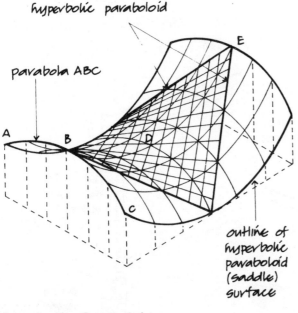

outline of straight line Limited hyperbolic paraboloid

parabola ABC

outline of hyperbolic paraboloid (saddle) surface

Hyperbolic Paraboloid (saddle) surface

Fig. 99

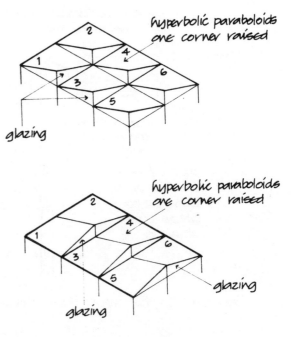

hyperbolic paraboloids one corner raised

glazing

hyperbolic paraboloids one corner raised

glazing

glazing

Hyperbolic paraboloid surfaces combined to form a roof

Fig. 100

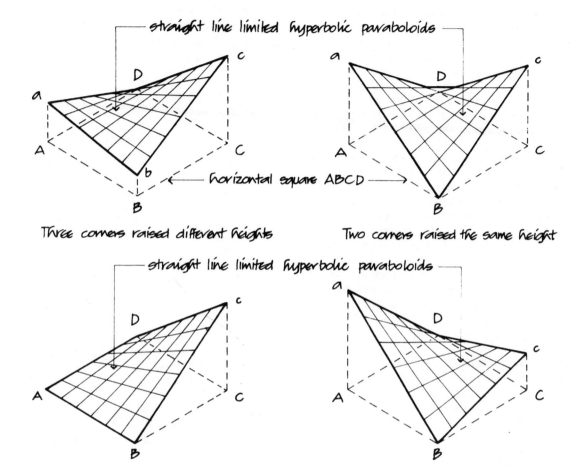

straight line limited hyperbolic paraboloids

D
c
a
A
C
b
horizontal square ABCD
B

Three corners raised different heights

a
c
D
A
C
B

Two corners raised the same height

straight line limited hyperbolic paraboloids

D
c
A
C
B

One corner raised

a
D
c
A
C
B

Two corners raised different heights

Setting out straight line limited hyperbolic paraboloid surfaces on a square base

Fig. 101

Hyperbolic paraboloid shells

The hyperbolic paraboloid concrete shells designed and constructed by Felix Candella in Mexico demonstrated the dramatic shapes and structural possibilities of doubly curved shells. This shape is formed when a parabolic generator moves along a parabolic directrix with the plane of the generator remaining vertical as it moves along the directrix (Fig. 99). The resulting surface is described as a hyperbolic paraboloid because horizontal sections through the surface are hyperbolas and vertical sections parabolas.

The structural significance of this shape is that at every point on the surface straight lines, which lie in the surface, intersect so that in effect the surface is made up of a net-

work of intersecting straight lines. In consequence the centering for a reinforced concrete hyperbolic paraboloid can consist of thin straight sections of timber which are simple to fix and support.

The most usual form of hyperbolic paraboloid roof is a straight line limited section of the shape illustrated in Fig. 101, the form being limited by straight lines for convenience in covering square plan shapes.

To set out straight line limited hyperbolic paraboloid surfaces it is only necessary to draw horizontal plane squares ABCD and lift one or more corners as illustrated in Fig. 101. The straight lines joining corresponding points on opposite sides set out the surface. The number of lines used to set out the surface is not material except that the more lines used the more clearly the surface will be revealed.

It will be seen from Fig. 101 that this surface is formed by concave downward parabolas running between high points 'a' and 'c' and concave upward parabolas between low points 'B' and 'D'. The amount by which the corners are raised will affect the curvature, shape and strength of the roof. The rise of a straight line limited hyperbolic paraboloid is the difference in height between the high and low points. If three corners are lifted differing heights, then the rise is the mean of the difference between the high and low points.

Obviously if the rise is small there will be little curvature of the shell which will then behave like a plane surface or plate and will need considerable thickness to resist deflection under load. The economic limit of least rise of this shell form is a rise of not less than one fifteenth of the diagonal span, that is the horizontal distance 'AC' in Fig. 101. The greater the rise the less the required thickness of shell.

Straight line limited hyperbolic paraboloids can be combined to provide a structure with rooflights fixed in the spandrel between adjacent shells (Fig. 100), where a number of similar separate hyperbolic paraboloid surfaces are combined to form a roof with spandrel glazing.

Reinforced concrete hyperbolic paraboloid shell: Fig. 102 is an illustration of an umbrella roof formed from four hyperbolic paraboloid surfaces supported on one column. The small section reinforcing mesh in the surface of the shell resists tensile and compressive stress and the heavier reinforcement around the edges and between the four hyperbolic paraboloid surfaces resists shear forces developed by the tensile and compressive stress in the shell. A series of these umbrella roofs are combined, with roof glazing between them, to give cover to the floor area below.

Timber hyperbolic paraboloid shell: A hyperbolic paraboloid shell can be formed with three layers of boards nailed together and glued around the edges with laminated edge beams, as illustrated in Fig. 103. It will be seen that the boards do not follow the straight lines lying in the surface of the shell. If they did they would have to be bent along their length and twisted across their width. As it is difficult to twist a board across its width and maintain it in that position, the boards are fixed as shown where they have to be bent only along their length. The timber edge beams, formed by glueing and screwing boards together, resist shear. Low points of the shell are anchored to concrete abutments to prevent the shell spreading under load.

The advantage of a timber shell is its low density of 25 kg/m^2 as compared to the density of 150 kg/m^2 for a similar concrete shell and the better insulation of the timber.

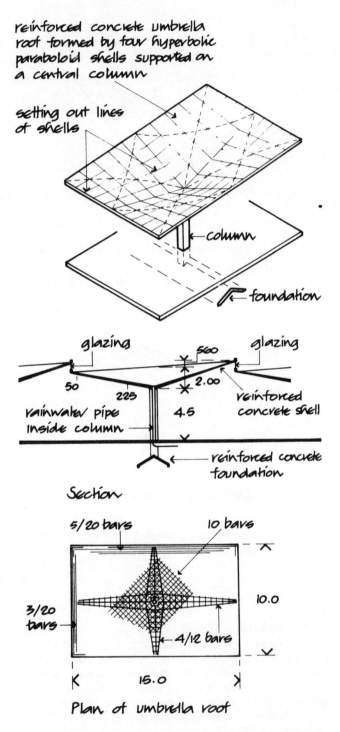

reinforced concrete umbrella roof formed by four hyperbolic paraboloid shells supported on a central column

setting out lines of shells

column

foundation

glazing — 560 — glazing

50 — 225 — 2.00 — reinforced concrete shell

rainwater pipe inside column — 4.5

reinforced concrete foundation

Section

5/20 bars — 10 bars

3/20 bars — 4/12 bars — 10.0

15.0

Plan of umbrella roof

Reinforced concrete hyperbolic paraboloid

Fig. 102

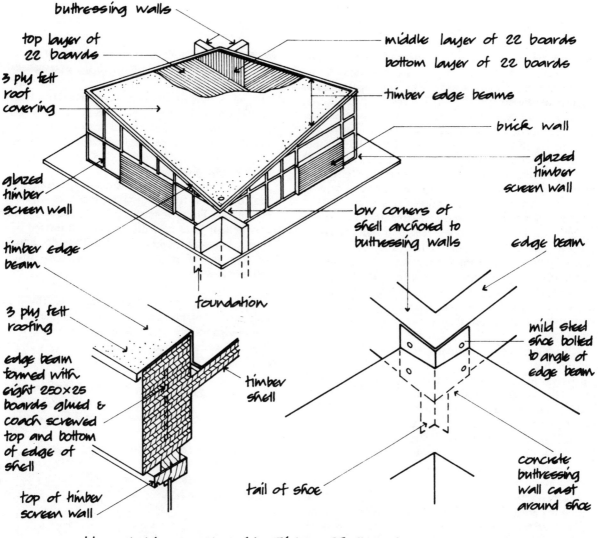

buttressing walls

top layer of 22 boards

3 ply felt roof covering

middle layer of 22 boards
bottom layer of 22 boards

timber edge beams

brick wall

glazed timber screen wall

glazed timber screen wall

low corners of shell anchored to buttressing walls

timber edge beam

foundation

edge beam

3 ply felt roofing

edge beam formed with eight 250×25 boards glued & coach screwed top and bottom of edge of shell

timber shell

top of timber screen wall

tail of shoe

mild steel shoe bolted to angle of edge beam

concrete buttressing wall cast around shoe

Hyperbolic paraboloid Timber Shell roof

Fig. 103

CHAPTER FIVE

DIAPHRAGM AND FIN WALL CONSTRUCTION

Brickwork has for centuries been the traditional material for the walls of houses and other small buildings. A one brick thick wall of well burned bricks, bonded and laid in a mortar of the same density and porosity as the bricks, has more than adequate strength to support the comparatively small loads from the floors and roof of a house, and sufficient stability in resisting the lateral pressure of wind. The wall, either solid or more usually as a cavity wall, will resist penetration of rain, have good resistance to damage by fire, require very little maintenance and have a useful life in excess of more than a hundred years.

Brickwork has good compressive strength in supporting vertical loads but poor tensile strength in resisting lateral pressure from the lateral loads of floors and roof and wind pressure. The minimum thickness of walls is prescribed in The Building Regulations by reference to the height and length of walls so that the greater the height of wall the greater the thickness the wall has to be at its base, to resist the lateral forces that tend to overturn it (see Volume 1).

A brick wall acts structurally as a vertical cantilever, rising vertically from its fixed base on the foundation so that lateral forces, such as wind, tend to cause the wall to bend. This bending is resisted by the small tensile strength of the brickwork, lateral restraint by floors and roof built into the wall and by buttressing walls and piers built into the wall (see Volume 1). The higher the wall, the greater the vertical cantilever arm of the wall and the thicker the wall needs to be at its base to resist overturning caused by lateral forces.

The majority of tall, single-storey buildings, enclosing large open areas, such as sports halls, warehouses, supermarkets and factories with walls of more than 5.0 in height were until recently built with a frame of lattice steel or a portal frame covered with steel or asbestos cement sheeting, insulation and a protective inner lining. Of recent years brick diaphragm or fin walls have been increasingly used for this type of building for the economy, durability, resistance to fire and penetration of rain and thermal and sound insulation advantages of such structures.

A diaphragm wall is built with two leaves of brickwork bonded to brick cross ribs or diaphragms inside a wide cavity between the leaves so that the wall is formed of a series of stiff box or I sections structurally as illustrated in Fig. 104.

A fin wall is built as a conventional cavity wall buttressed with piers or fins bonded to the external leaf of the cavity wall to buttress or stiffen the wall against overturning. A fin wall acts structurally as a series of T sections, as illustrated in Fig. 104. The effective width of the flange of the T section, that is the outer leaf, may be less than the centres of the fins for design calculations.

Brick diaphragm walls

The economic advantage of a diaphragm wall, in comparison to a portal frame structure, increases with the height of the wall. For wall heights of up to about 5.0 there is no cost benefit in using a diaphragm wall instead of a portal frame. For wall heights of over 5.0 the diaphragm wall is an economic alternative to a portal frame structure for tall, single-storey, single-cell buildings.

Strength: The compressive strength of the bricks and mortar of a diaphragm wall is considerable in relation to the comparatively small dead load of the wall, roof and imposed loads of wind and snow.

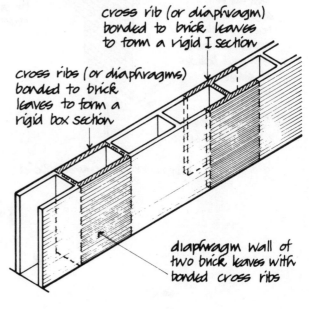

cross rib (or diaphragm) bonded to brick leaves to form a rigid I section

cross ribs (or diaphragms) bonded to brick leaves to form a rigid box section

diaphragm wall of two brick leaves with bonded cross ribs

Fig. 104

DIAPHRAGM AND FIN WALL CONSTRUCTION

Stability: A diaphragm wall is designed for stability through the width of the cavity and the spacing of the cross ribs to act as a series of stiff box or I sections and by the roof which is tied to the top of the wall to act as a horizontal plate to resist lateral forces.

Construction: The width of the cavity and the spacing of the cross ribs is determined by the box or I section required for stability and the need for economy in the use of materials by using whole bricks whenever possible. Cross ribs are usually spaced four or five whole brick lengths (with mortar joints) apart and the cavity one-and-a-half or two-and-a-half whole bricks (with mortar joints) apart so that the cross ribs can be bonded in alternate courses to the outer and inner leaves. Fig. 105 is an illustration of the bonding of typical diaphragm walls. It will be seen that the stretcher bond of the leaves is broken by header faces where the cross ribs are bonded in alternate courses. The colour of the header faces of many bricks is noticeably different from that of the stretcher faces so that in a diaphragm wall where the cross ribs are bonded to the leaves there is a distinct pattern on the wall faces. This pattern can be avoided, for appearance sake, by bonding the cross ribs to either one or both of the leaves with metal shear ties built into the cross ribs and the leaves.

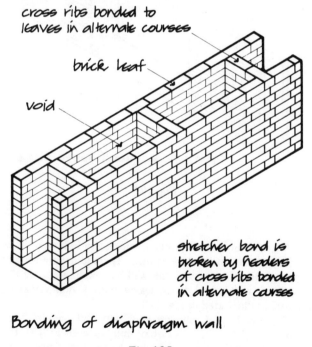

cross ribs bonded to leaves in alternate courses

brick leaf

void

stretcher bond is broken by headers of cross ribs bonded in alternate courses

Bonding of diaphragm wall

Fig. 105

The loads on the foundation of a diaphragm wall are so slight that a continuous concrete strip foundation is used for walls built on most natural undisturbed subsoils. A concrete strip foundation to a diaphragm wall is illustrated in Fig. 106. The width of the foundation is determined

from the load on the foundation and the safe bearing capacity of the subsoil (see Volume 1).

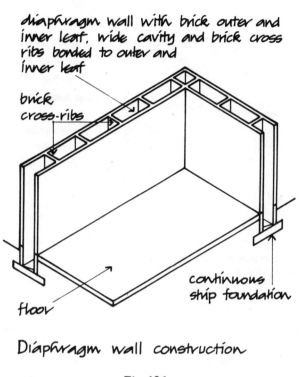

diaphragm wall with brick outer and inner leaf, wide cavity and brick cross ribs bonded to outer and inner leaf

brick cross-ribs

floor

continuous strip foundation

Diaphragm wall construction

Fig. 106

The roof of a diaphragm wall is tied to the top of the wall to act as a prop in resisting the overturning action of lateral wind pressure, by transferring the horizontal forces on the long walls to the end walls of the building that act as shear walls. To ensure that the roof structure is tied to the whole of the length of the top of walls, a reinforced concrete capping beam is cast or bedded on the top of the wall and the roof beams are bolted to the capping beam as illustrated in Fig. 107. It will be seen from Fig. 107 that the reinforced concrete capping beam does not project to the external face of the wall. This is solely for the sake of appearance.

The capping beam can be of reinforced, in-situ cast, concrete on a support of asbestos cement sheet. The disadvantage of this method of construction is the near impossibility of preventing wet cement stains disfiguring fairface brick surfaces below. To avoid unsightly stains on brickwork a system of pre-cast reinforced concrete capping beams is used. The beam is cast in lengths suited to the convenience of transport and handling and to span between cross ribs. The sections are tied with end ties or anchor bolts cast into the ends of sections and the joint is made with cement grout. Roof beams are tied to the capping beam with studs cast in the beam to which the beam is bolted as illustrated in Fig. 107.

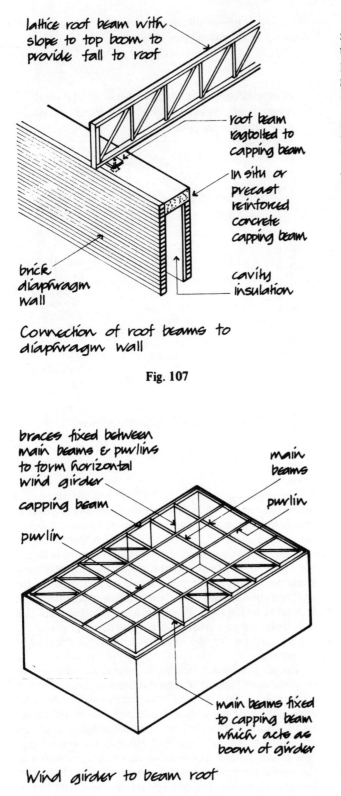

lattice roof beam with slope to top boom to provide fall to roof

roof beam ragbolted to capping beam

In situ or precast reinforced concrete capping beam

brick diaphragm wall

cavity insulation

Connection of roof beams to diaphragm wall

Fig. 107

braces fixed between main beams & purlins to form horizontal wind girder

capping beam

purlin

main beams

purlin

main beams fixed to capping beam which acts as boom of girder

Wind girder to beam roof

Fig. 108

The roof is tied to the capping beam to act as a horizontal prop to the top of the wall by transferring loads to the end walls. So that roof beams act together as a stiff plate they are braced by horizontal lattice steel wind girders connected to the roof beams, as illustrated in Fig. 108.

Door and window openings in diaphragm walls should preferably be designed to fit between the cross ribs so that the ribs can form the jamb of the opening. Large door and window openings will cause large local loading at the jambs from beam end bearings over the openings. Double ribs or thicker ribs are built at the jambs of large openings, to take the additional load, as illustrated in Fig. 109. Reinforced concrete lintels, the full thickness of the wall, are cast or bedded over openings.

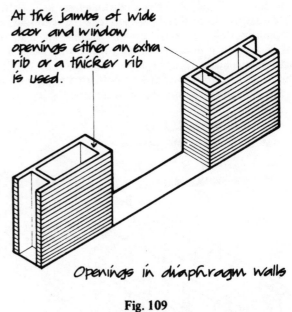

At the jambs of wide door and window openings either an extra rib or a thicker rib is used.

Openings in diaphragm walls

Fig. 109

Vertical movement joints are necessary in long walls to accommodate thermal movement. These joints are formed through the thickness of the wall by building double ribs to form a joint which is sealed with a non-hardening mastic as illustrated in Fig. 110.

A long, high diaphragm wall with flat parallel brick leaves may have a somewhat dull apperance. The flat surfaces of the wall can be broken by the use of projecting brick piers and a brick plinth, as illustrated in Fig. 111, where selected cross ribs project from the face of the wall, purely for appearance sake. As an alternative the external face of the wall can be indented by variations in the width of the cavity as illustrated in Fig. 112. The width and the depth of the breaks in the wall face are chosen for appearance.

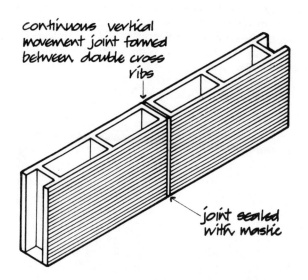

continuous vertical movement joint formed between double cross ribs

joint sealed with mastic

Movement joint in diaphragm wall

Fig. 110

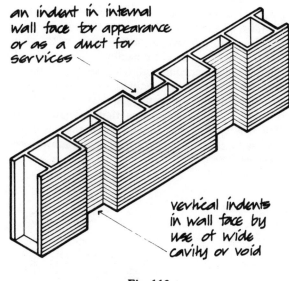

an indent in internal wall face for appearance or as a duct for services

vertical indents in wall face by use of wide cavity or void

Fig. 112

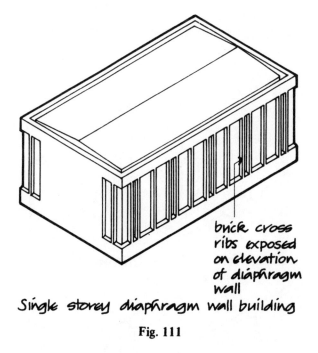

brick cross ribs exposed on elevation of diaphragm wall

Single storey diaphragm wall building

Fig. 111

Exclusion of rain: Experience of diaphragm walls built in positions of severe exposure and recent tests carried out, show that a diaphragm wall will satisfactorily resist penetration of rain water to the inner face of the wall. In positions of severe exposure there may be some penetration of rain into the brick cross ribs. To assist drying out of the cross ribs, by evaporation, it may be wise to ventilate the voids in the wall.

A continuous horizontal damp proof course (d.p.c.) should be built into a diaphragm wall for both leaves and cross ribs at floor level and at least 150 above ground level. Bitumen felt d.p.c.'s, which have poor resistance to compression, may squeeze out under heavy loads, whereas the more expensive brick d.p.c. of three courses of engineering bricks will provide good resistance to tensile stress at the base of the wall.

At the jambs of openings it is practice to build in a vertical d.p.c. of bitumen felt.

Thermal insulation: The thermal insulation of a diaphragm wall is some 10% less than that of a conventional cavity wall due to the circulation of air in the voids in the wall. The common method of improving the thermal insulation of a diaphragm wall is by fixing insulating boards, 75 or 100 thick, inside the voids against the inner leaf. The insulating boards are secured in position behind wall ties built into the cross ribs or with galvanised nails driven into the inner leaf.

The roof of diaphragm wall structures should act as a horizontal plate to prop the top of the wall against lateral forces. Some form of flat roof construction of main beams with or without secondary beams is most suited to act as a plate. Solid-web castellated or lattice main beams spanning the least width of the building, with horizontal wind girders, is the usual roof construction, with metal decking, insulation and built-up bitumen felt roof covering. Laminated timber main beams are used for the appearance of the natural material of the beams which are exposed.

Where pitched roof construction is used the frames of the roof structure should be braced to act as horizontal or near horizontal wind girders to prop the walls.

Brick fin walls

A fin wall is a conventional cavity wall buttressed by brick fins bonded to the outer leaf and projecting from the external face of the wall to stiffen high walls against horizontal pressures. Fig. 113 is an illustration of part of a fin wall. The minimum dimensions and spacing of the fins are determined by the cross sectional area of the T section of the wall required to resist the tensile stress from lateral pressure and by considerations of the appearance of the building. The spacing and dimensions of the fins can be varied to suit a chosen external appearance.

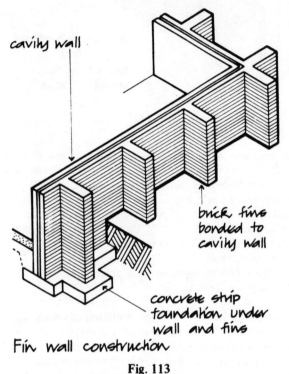

Fin wall construction

Fig. 113

For walls over about 5.0, a fin wall is used instead of a diaphragm wall because of the effect of the protruding vertical fins illustrated in Fig. 114 which can be built in a variety of ways for appearance sake. Some typical profiles for brick fins are illustrated in Fig. 115. For best effect, special bricks are used. These special bricks can be selected from the range of 'specials' produced by brickmakers or they can be specially made to order. The use of 'specials' will provide a better finish to brickwork than is possible by cutting standard bricks to the required shape. The use of special bricks does considerably increase the cost of brickwork.

Strength: The strength of the brickwork of a fin wall is considerable in relation to the comparatively small dead load of the wall and roof and imposed loads of wind and snow.

Stability: Stability against lateral forces from wind pressure is provided by the T section of the fins and the prop effect of the roof, which is usually tied to the top of the wall to act as a horizontal plate to transfer moments to the end walls.

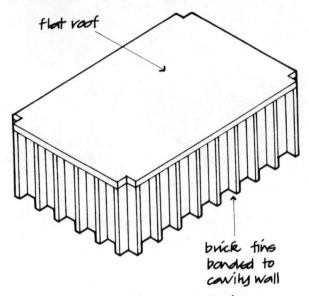

Single storey fin wall building

Fig. 114

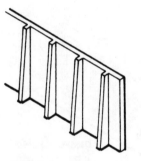
Tapered fins

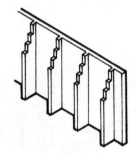
Stepped fins

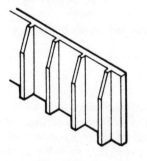
Bevelled fins

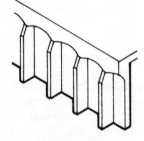
Brick arches & fins

Fig. 115

Construction: The wall is constructed as a conventional cavity wall with a 50 cavity and inner and outer leaves of brick tied with wall ties. The fins, which are bonded to the outer leaf in alternate courses, are usually one brick thick with a projection of four or more brick lengths. The fins should be spaced a number of whole bricks apart to minimise cutting of bricks and at centres necessary for stability and for appearance.

The loads on the foundation of a fin wall are so slight that a continuous concrete strip foundation will provide support and stability for the wall on most natural subsoils. A continuous strip foundation to a fin wall is illustrated in Fig. 116, from which it will be seen that the foundation is spread under the wall and extended under the fins.

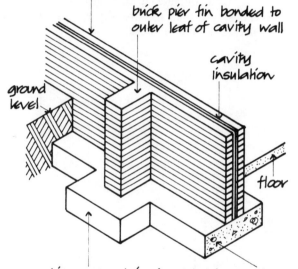

cavity wall with brick outer and brick inner leaf

brick pier fin bonded to outer leaf of cavity wall

cavity insulation

ground level

floor

continuous strip foundation under cavity wall and brick fin

Fin wall and foundation

Fig. 116

The roof of a fin wall is usually designed as a horizontal plate which props the top of the wall to transfer lateral pressures and so achieve an economy in the required wall section. Roof beams generally coincide with the centres of the fins, the roof beams being tied either to a continuous reinforced concrete capping beam cast or bedded on the wall or to concrete padstones cast or bedded on the fins as illustrated in Fig. 117. To resist wind uplift on light-weight roofs the beams are anchored to the brick fins through bolts built into the fins, cast or threaded through the padstones and bolted to the beams (Fig. 117).

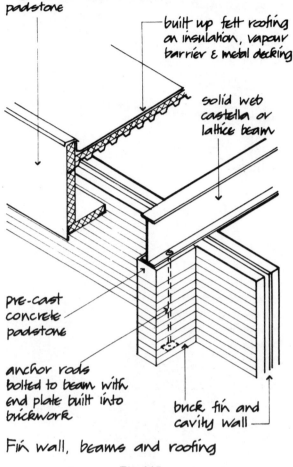

coated metal fascia and soffite screwed to angle frame fixed to beam & brackets in padstone

built up felt roofing on insulation, vapour barrier & metal decking

solid web castella or lattice beam

pre-cast concrete padstone

anchor rods bolted to beam with end plate built into brickwork

brick fin and cavity wall

Fin wall, beams and roofing

Fig. 117

Horizontal bracing to the roof beams is provided by lattice wind girders fixed to the beams to act as a plate in propping the top of the wall. These wind girders are usually combined with a capping plate to the top of fin walls.

Door and window openings in fin walls should be the same as the width between fins for simplicity of construction. To allow sufficient cross section of brickwork at the jambs of wide openings either a thicker fin or a double fin is built, as illustrated in Fig. 118. Movement joints, which are necessary in long walls, are formed between double brick fins as illustrated in Fig. 119.

Exclusion of rain: The cavity wall serves as a barrier to the penetration of rain to the inside face of the wall in all but positions of severe exposure. To an extent the projecting fins serve to disperse driving rain and thus give some protection to the cavity wall.

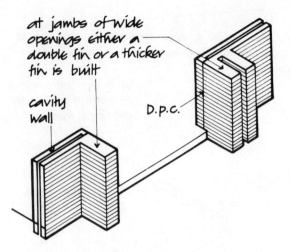

at jambs of wide
openings either a
double fin or a thicker
fin is built

cavity
wall

D.p.c.

Openings in fin walls

A continuous horizontal damp proof course must be built into the wall and the fins at floor level and at least 150 above ground. The considerations of the choice of materials is the same as that for diaphragm walls.

Thermal insulation: The insulation of the cavity wall is usually improved by the use of insulation bats fixed in the cavity against the inner leaf of the wall or by the use of cavity fill.

Blockwork walls
The majority of diaphragm and fin walls are built of brick because the small unit of the brick facilitates bonding and the construction of fins, recesses and cross ribs. Both diaphragm and fin walls can be built of concrete blocks, where the spacing of cross ribs and fins and width of voids is adapted to the block dimensions to minimise wasteful cutting of blocks. Because of the larger size of blocks, a wall of blocks will tend to have a more massive appearance than a similar wall of bricks.

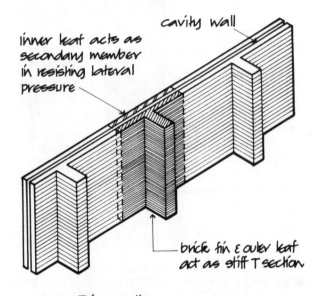

cavity wall

inner leaf acts as
secondary member
in resisting lateral
pressure

brick fin & outer leaf
act as stiff T section

Fin wall

Fig. 118

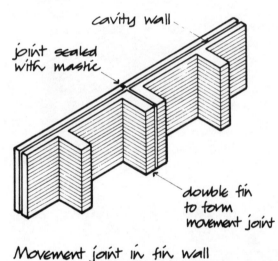

cavity wall

joint sealed
with mastic

double fin
to form
movement joint

Movement joint in fin wall

Fig. 119

CHAPTER SIX

THERMAL INSULATION

The Building Regulations (First Amendment) 1978 Part FF set minimum standards for the insulation of buildings, for the conservation of fuel and power in buildings other than dwellings, by prescribing maximum U values for walls, floors and roofs. The purpose groups of buildings affected by the (First Amendment) 1978 are listed below.

Purpose group

II	Institutional
III	Other residential
IV	Offices
V	Shops
VI	Factories
VII	Other places of assembly
VIII	Storage and general.

Details of the uses of buildings that are included in each purpose group are set out in the table to Regulation E2 of The Building Regulations 1976.

The maximum U value for walls, floors and roofs for purpose groups II, III, IV, V, VII and VIII (not for storage) is 0.6 W/m^2°C and that for purpose groups VI and VIII (for storage) is 0.7 W/m^2°C.

The U value is defined as the thermal transmittance coefficient, that is to say, the rate of heat transfer calculated in watts through one square metre of a structure when the combined radiant and air temperature at each side of the structure differs by 1°C.

Thermal transmittance: The U value defines the quantity of heat that will flow through unit area in unit time with unit difference in temperature. The U value, which is expressed as $U = \frac{1}{R}$ W/m^2°C, is the reciprocal of thermal resistance.

Thermal resistance: R, which is expressed as $R = \frac{t}{k}$, where t is the thickness in metres and k is the thermal conductivity.

Thermal conductivity: This is the rate of flow of heat through a material when a difference exists between the temperatures of its surfaces. The units of thermal conductivity are W/m°C.

The U value, or thermal transmittance, is an expression of the rate of heat flow through unit area so that the larger the value of U the less the resistance to heat flow and the poorer the insulation, and conversely, the smaller the value of U the better the insulation against heat flow.

By setting a maximum U value for the walls, floors and roofs of buildings, The Building Regulations set a minimum value for insulation.

The thin sheet materials glass and plastic used for windows and rooflights have a high U value and readily transmit heat. Recognising the need for daylight in buildings and the poor insulation of glazing materials, The Building Regulations (First Amendment) 1978 Part FF set maximum areas for windows and rooflights as a compromise between minimising heat loss and the need for daylight. The maximum area of a window and rooflight opening is taken as the area of the window and rooflight measured over the inner surface of the element. The areas set out in Table 1 of the regulations are shown in the following table.

Maximum area of window and rooflight openings expressed as a percentage of the total areas of walls and roofs

Purpose group	II or III	IV, V or VII	VI or VIII
Window opening	25	35	15
Rooflight opening	20	20	20

These prescribed maximum areas for windows and rooflights can be increased proportionally where double or triple glazing is used, to the extent that the total heat loss through the wall or roof does not exceed the loss that would have occurred if the window or rooflight had been single glazed. Where the area of rooflights is less than the maximum set out in the table, then the area of window may be increased above the maximum provided the total heat loss is not increased.

Insulation: The materials or combinations of materials used in the construction of walls and roofs do not generally by themselves provide sufficient resistance to the transfer of heat to satisfy the maximum U values prescribed in The Building Regulations, and it is usually necessary to add some material with a high insulating value to walls and roofs to raise the insulation to the required U value. Most materials with a good thermal resistance and a low U value are light-weight and porous and have poor mechanical strength so that they have to be supported by the roof or wall covering or sandwiched between sheets or leaves of the structural materials.

The consequence of the adoption of high standards of insulation for the envelope of buildings has been to greatly increase the temperature range to which those parts of the roofs and walls that are on the outside of insulation become subject and to increase dimensional changes and the effect of condensation in roofs and walls.

The very considerable dimensional changes that flat roof coverings, laid over insulation, are subjected to by changes of temperature, have been a prime cause of the failure of flat roof coverings.

The temperature differential between the warm moist inside air of buildings and the cold outside air has caused degradation of steel and timber and of the insulating materials themselves by the condensation of moisture vapour from warm inside air on the colder surfaces of the material of roofs and walls. The dimensional changes of those parts of roofs and walls that are outside the insulation layer can be provided for in the overlap of roof and wall coverings and by improvements in the materials of and fixing of flat roof coverings.

Condensation can be controlled by ventilation of air spaces and by fixing impermeable layers of some sheet material as vapour checks or vapour barriers between the warm moist inside air and the cold parts of roofs and walls.

Condensation

The limited capacity of air to hold moisture in the form of water vapour increases with temperature. The temperature at which air reaches the limit of its capacity to hold moisture and is fully saturated with water vapour, is called the dew point. When the temperature of air, that is fully saturated with water vapour at dew point, falls, so does its capacity to hold moisture and the surplus moisture is given up in the form of dew or condensation.

Moisture vapour in air exerts a pressure, termed vapour pressure. The ratio of the vapour pressure of moisture in air relative to the vapour pressure of moisture in fully saturated air at the same temperature is called the relative humidity (RH) and is expressed as a percentage. With a relative humidity of 80%, air is holding four fifths of its capacity to hold moisture vapour at the same temperature.

Surface condensation: Occurs when the temperature of warm moist air falls, by contact with a cold surface, to or below the dew point temperature for the vapour moisture held in the air, so that the surplus moisture vapour condenses to moisture on the cold surface. The warm moist air of a bathroom condenses on the surface of cold glass in windows, condensation drips from hook bolts fixed through roof sheeting and insulation because the steel hook bolts act as a cold bridge between the cold outside air and the warm moist inside air of the building.

Surface condensation may occur on the underside of metal roof sheeting fixed over a layer of insulation when the warm moist air inside a building penetrates the

joints between the insulation and condenses on the cold underside of the sheets. The form of construction in which roof or wall sheeting is fixed over insulation is sometimes described as cold construction or a cold roof.

Cold construction or a cold roof: It is so named because the sheeting is in contact with the cold outside air, as illustrated in Fig. 120. The term cold construction is not a particularly meaningful expression as it refers to the position of the principal insulation layer in the thickness of roof construction and its effect on the temperature of those parts of the roof outside the insulation rather than the temperature of the roof itself.

The control of surface condensation on the underside of sheet metal roof coverings fixed over an insulating layer in the typical single-storey construction illustrated in Fig. 120, is effected by the use of a vapour check fixed under the insulation or by ventilating the air space between the insulation and the sheeting or both.

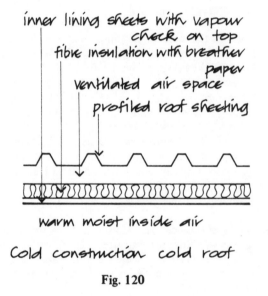

Protected membrane roof

inner lining sheets with vapour check on top
fibre insulation with breather paper
ventilated air space
profiled roof sheeting

warm moist inside air

Cold construction cold roof

Fig. 120

Vapour check and vapour barrier: To reduce the movement of warm moist air from inside a building to the space between the insulation and the roof sheeting, it is practice to fix a layer of some impermeable material, such as polythene sheeting, to the underside of the insulation or to use the material of the underlining supporting the insulation as a check to the movement of water vapour. By definition a vapour check is any material that is sufficiently impermeable to check the movement of water vapour without being an unbroken continuous barrier to water vapour which may penetrate the joints between the sheets or lining forming the vapour check.

THERMAL INSULATION

A vapour barrier is a continuous, unbroken layer or sheet of impermeable material that serves as a complete barrier to the movement of water vapour in air. Because of the practical difficulties of making an airtight joint between sheets or underlining materials and around rooflights and pipes, it is in effect impossible to make an airtight vapour barrier.

Another approach to reducing the likelihood of condensation on the underside of roof sheeting fixed over an insulating layer is to form a definite and continuous air space between the sheeting and the insulation which is positively ventilated to the outside so that movement of air through the space will prevent the build-up of water vapour and the likelihood of condensation. For the ventilated air space to be effective there must be an adequate open area on each side of the air space to allow a free flow of air. Natural cross ventilation depends on wind speed and direction and it is impossible to predict the area of openings required to encourage ventilation, particularly as in still, cold weather air is often static just when ventilation is most needed. Experience suggests that the area of opening required for cross ventilation should be equivalent to 4% of the plan area of a roof and that openings should be 10 wide to allow unrestricted flow of air.

Where fibre or open-cell insulation materials are used below a ventilated air space, there will be a reduction in the insulating effect by the cold ventilating air penetrating the insulation. To reduce this effect the top surface of fibre or open-cell insulants should be covered with 'breather paper' to reduce the movement of cold air into the insulation and at the same time allow moisture vapour to pass through the insulation and breather paper to the ventilated space.

The construction of a 'cold roof' with roof sheeting over an insulating layer, with a ventilated air space, breather paper to the top of the insulation and a vapour check to the internal lining is illustrated in Fig. 120.

Interstitial condensation: Moisture vapour in air exerts a pressure that is known as vapour pressure. The air inside most heated buildings contains more water vapour than outside air and so has a higher vapour pressure which creates a vapour drive from the area of high pressure inside the building to the outside through the materials of roofs and walls. In cold weather the temperature of the covering of a flat roof laid on a layer of insulation will fall. Due to differences of vapour pressure between inside and outside air the insulation under the roof covering may contain water vapour which may condense due to the fall in temperature. This effect is known as interstitial condensation, that is, condensation in the interstices or small cells or spaces or crevices in materials.

Warm construction or a warm roof: The form of construction illustrated in Fig. 121 is sometimes described as a warm roof or warm construction because the deck that supports the covering and the insulation is maintained

at the inside air temperature by the insulation above it, and is therefore much less subject to surface condensation than it would be were the insulation below it. Because of the difference of water vapour pressure between the warm inside air and the cold outside air there will be a vapour drive from inside to outside. The water vapour drive will cause a slow and continuous movement of water vapour through the roof, upwards when the outside temperature is below inside temperature, and downwards when outside is above inside temperature.

In winter, when the outside temperature is much below the inside temperature, the water vapour in the insulation under the roof covering may condense to moisture in the insulating material in the form of interstitial condensation. Continuous wetting of insulation materials of organic fibre can cause decay from fungal growth and loss of strength and will cause a reduction in insulation of all materials that absorb moisture.

To reduce the likelihood of damage and reduction in insulation by interstitial condensation it is practice to fix a layer or sheet of some impermeable material below the insulation to act as a vapour check as illustrated in Fig. 121.

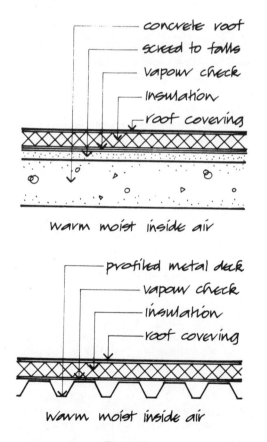

Fig. 121

Protected membrane roof: This is a form of warm roof with the insulation laid on top of the waterproof covering and held in position by a layer of gravel or paving slabs as illustrated in Fig. 122. The advantage of this form of construction is that the roof covering is protected by the insulation from the movements associated with temperature changes that cause breakdown of the covering. The disadvantage is that the covering is not accessible for inspection and any necessary repair or renewal of the covering is made more expensive by the need to take up and replace the insulation and surface loading layer. The insulation layer has to be one of the closed cell materials that do not absorb rainwater which drains through the surface loading and the insulation to the waterproof covering.

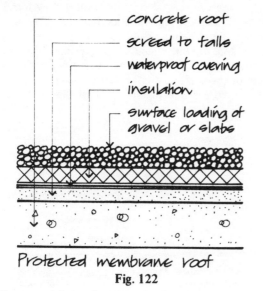

concrete roof
screed to falls
waterproof covering
insulation
surface loading of gravel or slabs

Protected membrane roof
Fig. 122

The materials used principally for their thermal insulation properties are:

Mineral fibre: This is manufactured from crushed and graded volcanic rock that is melted at high temperature. The molten rock is drawn through small apertures to form long, fine fibres. The fibres are spread to form a loose mat which is sprayed with a resin to bind the fibres. The mat of mineral wool is then passed through rollers to compress it to flexible rolled mat, semi-rigid or rigid slabs, and then through heated ovens to cure the resin.

Mineral wool is dimensionally stable, non-hygroscopic, odourless, does not support fungal or mould growth, has excellent thermal resistance, good sound absorption properties and is non-combustible.

Mineral wool in the form of a light-weight, resilient mat either unfaced or faced with building paper is used as an insulating lining to roofs where it is laid across underlining sheets on pitched roofs. The unfaced mat is classified as non-combustible.

Thermal conductivity: 0.04 W/m°C, density: 16 kg/m³.

Rigid mineral wool slabs of resin bonded long rock fibres are used as insulation for flat and sloping roofs as a base for asphalt and built-up roofing.

Thermal conductivity: 0.034 W/m°C, density: 64 and 96 kg/m³.

Glass fibre is manufactured by spinning molten glass into fine fibres that are matted and bound together with resin in the form of rolls of glass wool or compressed into rigid slabs of glass fibre.

Glass wool: dimensionally stable, odourless, non-hygroscopic, does not rot or support fungal or mould growth, has excellent thermal resistance and good sound absorption properties and is non-combustible.

Glass wool is supplied in rolls for use as an insulting mat that is laid over underlining sheets on pitched roofs.

Glass fibre slabs have moderate mechanical strength and are used as insulation under asphalt and built-up roof coverings on flat roofs.

Thermal conductivity: 0.04 W/m°C, density: 12 kg/m³.

Cellular glass: This is made from pure glass that is expanded twenty times to form rigid, cellular insulation slabs which are almost impermeable to water vapour, do not absorb water, are rot and vermin proof, dimensionally stable, non-combustible and have good compressive strength. The slabs, which are used as insulation for flat roofs, can be used without a vapour check if the joints are sealed with bitumen. These slabs serve as a stable base for asphalt and fully bonded built-up roofing.

Thermal conductivity: 0.04 W/m°C, density: 135 kg/m³.

Perlite: This is a mineral of volcanic origin that is combined with small quantities of water. When powdered perlite is heated the water in the mineral expands to form beads of perlite that are honeycombed with microscopic sealed air cells. The beads of perlite are combined with mineral fibres and binders to form a light-weight board, one surface of which is coated with a bitumen emulsion.

These boards have good dimensional stability and compressive strength but are somewhat brittle. The material will lose strength by the absorption of water. Perlite does not decay and is non-combustible. Because of their dimensional stability, these boards are used as a base for built-up roofing and asphalt either by themselves or as an overlay to one of the plastic insulation materials.

Thermal conductivity: 0.05 W/m°C, density: 175 kg/m³.

Polystyrene: This is used for insulation as boards of expanded beads of polystyrene that are fused together (bead board), as granular loose fill and as extruded polystyrene which is formed by a simultaneous extrusion and foaming process. The boards are used as insulating linings and the beads as loose fill to cavities.

Expanded polystyrene (bead board) is much used as an insulating lining to roofs because its thermal conductivity is lower than that of most other materials. The boards are competitively priced, easy to handle and cut and have sufficient compressive strength for use as an insulation board. The material is dimensionally unstable and should be covered with a layer of fibre board when used as a base for built-up roofing. The material which has a low melting point and softens and burns fairly rapidly, should be protected by an underlining when used as insulation under roofing.

Thermal conductivity: 0.037 W/m°C, density: 15 kg/m^3.

Extruded polystyrene boards which have exceptional resistance to water absorption, excellent thermal resistance and reasonable compressive strength are used as insulation in protected membrane roofs. They are dimensionally unstable and have a low melting point.

Thermal conductivity: 0.032 W/m°C, density: 30 kg/m^3.

Polyurethane and polyisocyanurate: Rigid boards are made by moulding or casting mixtures of polyether polyol resin and blowing agents with a mixture of polyisocynates which blow to form a foam of air-filled cells that are moulded to the form of slabs, boards and the shaped insulation sandwich in composite panels. These foamed plastic insulants are used in particular as the profiled insulation sandwich in composite profiled steel sheeting because of the ease of moulding the material and its excellent thermal resistance.

Foamed boards are usually faced on both sides with bitumised glass fibre when used as insulation for flat roofs. The materials have low water permeability, high resistance to most chemicals and good stability.

Thermal conductivity: 0.023 W/m°C, density: 35 kg/m^3.

Fibreboard: This was the original building board used as insulation in buildings. It is manufactured by felting wood and other vegetable fibres which are compressed to form rigid boards. The boards have moderate mechanical strength, moderate resistance to transfer of heat and good dimensional stability. The material, which readily absorbs moisture, loses strength and resistance to transfer of heat when saturated with water. These boards, which have poor resistance to damage by fire and spread of flame, are much less used than they were, being principally used as a base over a plastic insulation for asphalt and built-up roofing because of the low cost of the material and its dimensional stability.

Thermal conductivity: 0.06 W/m°C, density: 300 kg/m^3.

Corkboard: This is made from compressed cork granules that are held together by the natural cork gum. Cork boards have good compressive but poor tensile strength. The friable material requires careful handling and support at close centres. Cork, which is resistant to moisture and decay, is used in conditions of high humidity. These boards are comparatively expensive, have reasonable resistance to transfer of heat and moderate resistance to damage by fire.

Thermal conductivity: 0.034 W/m°C, density: 115 kg/m^3.

CHAPTER SEVEN

FLAT ROOFS

There is no economic or practical advantage in the use of a flat roof structure unless the roof is used as a deck for leisure, recreation or storage purposes.

A flat roof structure is less efficient structurally than a pitched roof structure and there is no saving in unused roof space in a flat roof as compared to a low pitch frame structure. The inevitable deflection of horizontal beams that would cause ponding of rainwater on flat roofs requires the construction of falls on the roof to clear rainwater to outlets. The many failures of flat roof coverings that have occurred do not tend to recommend the use of flat roofs.

None the less it has been fashionable for many years to construct large buildings with flat roofs for the sake of the horizontal roof line that was in favour.

The definition of a flat roof is a roof having a slope of up to 5 degrees to the horizontal, and a sloping roof is one with a slope of from 5 degrees up to 10 degrees to the horizontal.

It is generally accepted practice for flat roofs to be constructed with a surface that has a fall or slope of at least 1 in 80 to rainwater outlets so that rainwater will run off towards outlets. This fall is often increased to 1 in 60 or 1 in 40 to make allowance for deflection of beams and inaccuracies in construction.

Due to the self-weight of a roof construction and the imposed loads of wind and snow, every horizontal structure will deflect or sag at mid-span between points of support. It would therefore seem logical to accept this inevitable deflection as a means of providing the shallow fall or slope necessary to drain rainwater to outlets at mid-span. This sensible approach to design, in the utilisation of an inevitable structural effect, to drain a roof surface is not generally accepted because it is usually inconvenient to have rainwater down pipes running down inside buildings at the middle of the clear span of structures as the pipes will probably constrain freedom of layout of activities on floors and it is unsightly. It also invites blockages of rainwater pipes to run them with a fall under roofs down to external walls. The most convenient place to run rainwater down pipes is at points of support, such as columns and walls, just where the deflection of a roof is least and natural run-off of water will not occur.

For these reasons horizontal, flat roof structures must have some form of construction to provide a fall or slope to the roof surface to drain water to the necessary outlets fixed above points of support. The choice of a means of construction to provide a fall will depend on whether the roof surface is to fall in two directions to level central valleys and eaves or parapet gutters or to have falls in two directions to a central outlet as illustrated in Fig. 123. The junction of the falls in two directions, that form a shallow valley, is termed a current or cross fall. The more straightforward one-direction fall can be constructed with some form of tapered or pitched member such as lattice secondary beams with the top boom of the beams tapered or pitched at 1 in 60, with tapered firring pieces of wood laid on top of the beams or with insulation boards cut to a tapered section to provide a fall. The two-direction fall is more complex to construct because of the necessity to cut firring pieces or taper members to the mitre of the cross falls at the junction of falls running at right angles to each other (it should be noted that a wet screed spread on a deck of concrete can be readily spread and finished to cross falls).

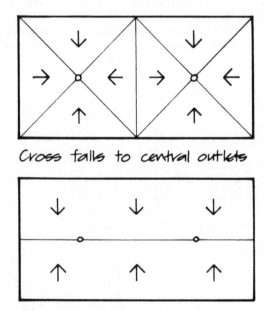

Cross falls to central outlets

Straight falls to outlets

Falls and drainage of flat roofs

Fig. 123

FLAT ROOFS

Flat roof coverings are usually designed to fall directly to rainwater outlets without the use of gutter or sumps formed below the surface of the roof. The run-off of rainwater from a flat roof is comparatively slow and regular and there is no advantage in the use of gutters or sumps to accelerate the flow of water and considerable disadvantage in the construction of gutters or sumps and the additional labour and joints necessary in finishing the roof covering around the drip edges of gutters and sumps. A typical straight-fall rainwater outlet is illustrated in Fig. 124, where the roof falls in two directions to a level valley that is drained by internal outlets above points of support of the structure with the down pipe run against a column.

The area of flat roof to be drained to rainwater outlets and the flow of water is determined by reference to maps of England showing areas of peak rainfall. The area of roof to be drained is usually based on the need to drain rainwater in periods of maximum fall. Calculations are commonly based on a fall of 75 mm per hour for two minutes, which fall occurs with a frequency on average every year in most of the more densely populated parts of the midlands and south of England.

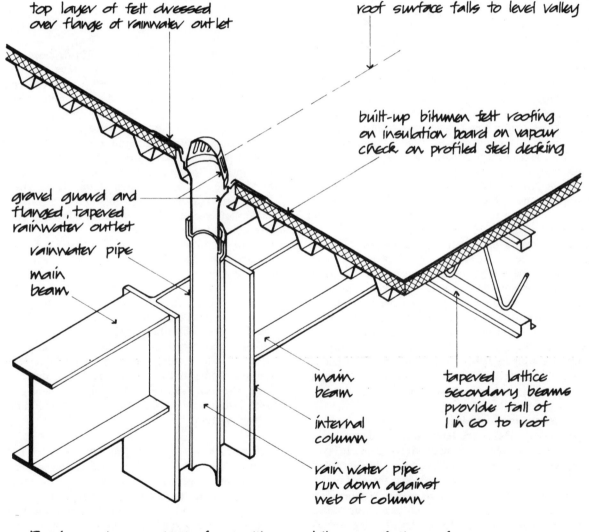

Rain water outlet in built-up bitumen felt roof

Fig. 124

Thermal insulation: The majority of flat roofs are constructed with a deck laid across the structural members of the roof. The deck acts as support for the flat roof covering below which a layer of some insulating material is laid. Because the insulation is above the deck, this form of roof construction is described as a 'warm roof' because the deck is insulated from the outside and will, therefore, tend to be maintained at the same temperature as the heated inside of buildings and be much less vulnerable to condensation than it would be were the insulation below the deck. The warm roof form of construction is of particular advantage where profiled steel decking is used as the support for the roof surface as the insulation above the deck greatly reduces the likelihood of warm moist air from the inside condensing on the surface of the metal deck. The disadvantage of the warm roof is that the insulation under the roof covering will increase the temperature differences of the covering between day and night and so increase elongation stress and fatigue of the covering.

The Building Regulations (First Amendment) 1978 Part FF set limits to the rate of heat loss or gain through roofs by mandatory standards of thermal transmittance by reference to a maximum U value for roof construction. To meet these requirements some form of insulation has to be included in the roof construction of the majority of flat roofs. The advantage of the flat roof deck form of construction is that the deck supports both the roof covering and the insulation, whereas with roof cladding sheet construction, the insulation, which is below the sheets, may require some form of support separate from the sheets.

Heated warm air inside buildings carries water vapour which will condense to moisture when in contact with cold surfaces. The moisture from the persistent condensation of water vapour will cause damage by the corrosion of metals and will also impair the efficiency of porous insulating materials that absorb moisture from condensation. With the warm roof form of construction for flat roofs, the decking is not likely to be subject to damage by condensation because it is covered with insulation and to some extent the decking acts as a barrier to the penetration of water vapour into the insulation above.

Materials for flat roof coverings

Built-up roofing: This is the term used to describe a roof covering which is built up on site with two or more layers of rolls of material that are laid over a prepared roof deck or sloping roof and which are bonded to the roof and to each other with an adhesive such as hot bitumen. The majority of the materials that are used for built-up roofing are described as built-up bitumen felt roofing because they have a reinforcing base of felt that is coated with bitumen. The nature of the reinforcing felt base, to a large extent controls the strength, weathering and durability of built-up bitumen felt roofing as a weather protection to roofs.

Bitumen felt roofing: The three bitumen roofing felts included in BS 747 are

Fibre-based bitumen felt. The traditional bitumen felt roofing is manufactured from cellulose fibres that are woven and compacted into a felt that is saturated in bitumen to protect the felt base and then coated on both sides with bitumen to provide a waterproof finish. In time the fibre-based felt will rot, due to the absorption of moisture, and lose so much of its strength as a reinforcement to the bitumen that it will no longer hold the bitumen together and the covering will fail as a weather protection. With improvements in felted bases and modifications of bitumen to improve the performance of felted roof coverings, the original fibre-based felt is used much less than it was. Its main uses are for short-life coverings to sheds and as the middle layer with other felt bases for economy.

Asbestos-fibre-based bitumen felt. This is more expensive than both fibre and glass-fibre-based felts. Although it is more resistant to loss of strength by the absorption of moisture than fibre-based felt it will in time lose strength and no longer act as a reinforcement for the bitumen coating. Because of the asbestos fibre base this felt maintains its integrity during fires for a longer period than other felts and it has been used either as one layer of built-up felt roofing or as a multi-layer system to improve the performance of coverings during fires. This felt is sometimes used on sloping roofs as the material can be nailed more successfully to sloping surfaces to secure the covering than other felt bases.

Since the introduction of glass-fibre-based felts, asbestos-fibre-based felts are used much less than they were for roofing.

Glass-fibre-based felt. This was first introduced in the 1950s. The glass tissue reinforcement of this felt is composed of glass fibres held together with an adhesive. The insoluble glass fibres do not lose strength as a reinforcement to the bitumen coating. Glass-fibre-based felt built-up roofing is the cheapest and most durable of the three felts included in BS 747. Three layers of glass-fibre-based bitumen felt roofing should have a useful life of up to twenty years.

High performance bitumen felt. This has a felt base with improved strength to resist elongation and provide a non-rotting base, together with modifications of bitumen to improve the ageing characteristics of ordinary bitumen which hardens and loses elasticity during the first three to five years of exposure to ultra-violet light, ozone and oxygen, with resulting loss of flexibility, strength and fatigue resistance.

These so-called high performance bitumen felts have a felted polyester fibre base, which has greater strength and elongation at break than glass fibre, is non-rotting and is stable for many years. The felted base is saturated and coated with elastomer modified bitumen incorporating a mineral filler and coated with sand on both sides. The addition of a polymer modifies and improves the flexibility, strength and fatigue-resistance of bitumen. The additives that are used are SBS (styrene butadiene styrene) and APP (atactic polypropylene). Felts with SBS additives which have the greatest elasticity are laid and fixed by the traditional pour-and-roll hot bitumen technique and those with APP additives (which have improved high temperature and weathering characteristics) are bonded by gas flame torching.

One of the sheet or membrane materials that is used for built-up bitumen roofing does not have a felted base. The sheet is composed of bitumen, synthetic rubber, polyethylene, hydocarbon resin, fillers and polymer fibres that are mixed in without being felted. The mix is heated, milled and calendered to a thin sheet. These sheets are used with bitumen felts for their resistance to light foot traffic, good impact resistance and greater elasticity and tensile strength than ordinary bitumen felts.

Loose-lay roofing sheets: These are made from plasticised polyvinyl chloride (PVC) which is converted to sheets by squeezing the molten polymer through a succession of rotating rollers that reduce it to a thin sheet of uniform thickness. This process of roll forming sheet material is called calendering. The sheet material, that is 1.5 mm thick, is impermeable to water, has a relatively high vapour permeability, good resistance to tearing, elongation at break and abrasion. These sheets are used as a loose-lay covering membrane to flat roofs.

Laying built-up bitumen felt roofing: Bitumen felt roofing is laid by pouring hot bitumen in front of the felt as it is unrolled across the roof so that the felt spreads the bitumen the full width of the roll. This traditional 'pour-and-roll' technique is used for each layer of felt, underlays, vapour checks and vapour barriers. The rolls of bitumen felt roofing are laid with 50 side laps and 100 end laps with laps staggered a third of a roll width between layers of built-up roofing for the sake of waterproofing and to avoid an excessive build-up of thickness of material.

The top layer or cap sheet of built-up bitumen felt roofing is usually surfaced with a range of coloured mineral aggregates which adhere to the bitumen coating and are used for the sake of appearance.

The dark, non-reflective surface of bitumen felt absorbs solar radiant heat which raises the temperature of the surface during the day and allows radiant heat loss at night. In consequence the roofing is subject to considerable temperature change and day by day cycles of softening and hardening, which cause fatigue and ageing of bitumen. To reduce the effects of temperature change, a reflective surface coating of mineral chippings is applied to the roof. A layer of 10 or 14 thick stone chippings is bonded to the surface in hot bitumen. The reflective properties of the light-coloured stone chippings reduces temperature changes and gives protection from ultraviolet light. The disadvantage of the stone chippings is that they may block rainwater outlets if a gravel guard, illustrated in Fig. 124, is not used.

Bitumen felt roofing with layers of felt, asbestos or glass fibre bases is usually laid as three layers for built-up roofing. The best quality of this type of roofing consists of three layers of glass-fibre-based felt. Combinations of felt bases are sometimes used which combine felt base layers with glass-fibre-based felts for the sake of economy.

The two methods of fixing the first layer of felt to the roof surface are by full bonding or partial bonding to the roof surface.

Fully bonded built-up roofing: This is used on wood fibreboard and cork surfaces to which the first layer of felt is fully bonded with hot bitumen by the pour-and-roll technique of laying, with subsequent layers being fully bonded to the layer below.

Partial bonding: Partial bonding of the bottom layer of built-up roofing is used on concrete, cement screeds, wood wool, plywood, chipboard, polyurethane and polyisocyanurate insulation board surfaces. A first layer of perforated glass-fibre-based gritted felt is laid loose on the roof surface without a bitumen bond. The next layer is then fully bonded to the first layer by the pour-and-roll technique so that the hot bitumen finds its way through the perforations in the first layer to form spot bonds to the roof surface. The reason for the use of a partial bond is to prevent moisture from being trapped locally under the first layer. The partial bond allows the moisture vapour to disperse. If a full bond were used there would be a likelihood of moisture being trapped locally and expanding when heated by the sun, so forming a blister that might rupture the covering.

Skirting and upstands: At upstands to parapets, abutments and curbs to rooflights, an upstand skirting at least 150 high is formed. To take out the sharp right-angled junction of roof and upstand, a timber, wood fibreboard or polyurethane angle fillet 50 × 75 is fixed so that the felt covering is not damaged by being turned up at a right angle. The first layer of felt is finished up to the angle fillet and the second and third layers are continued over the fillet and up as skirting, as shown in Fig. 125.

Eaves and verges: At eaves a welted drip is formed with a strip of mineral-faced felt that is nailed to a timber batten, bent to form a drip edge and bonded into the built-up roofing as illustrated in Fig. 126.

At verges an edge upstand is formed with timber or in the roof surface to prevent water running off the roof, and the built-up roofing is dressed over the verge (Fig. 126).

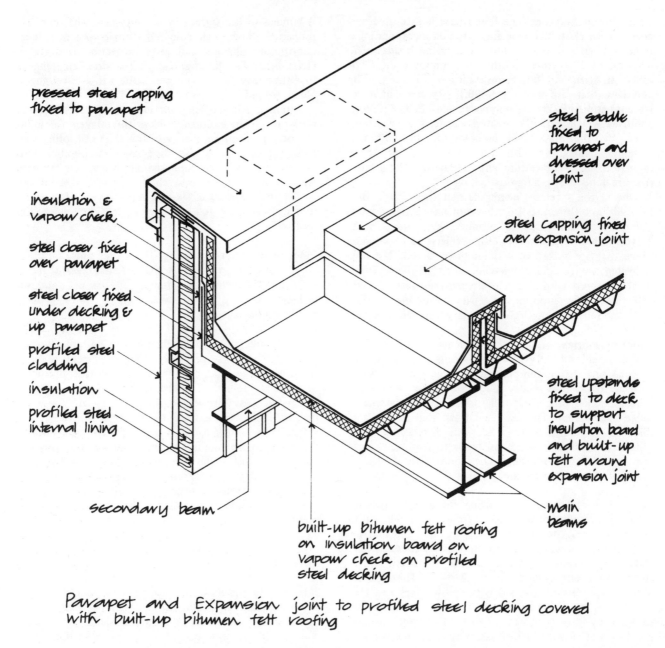

pressed steel capping fixed to parapet

insulation & vapour check

steel closer fixed over parapet

steel closer fixed under decking & up parapet

profiled steel cladding

insulation

profiled steel internal lining

secondary beam

steel saddle fixed to parapet and dressed over joint

steel capping fixed over expansion joint

steel upstands fixed to deck to support insulation board and built-up felt around expansion joint

main beams

built-up bitumen felt roofing on insulation board on vapour check on profiled steel decking

Parapet and Expansion joint to profiled steel decking covered with built-up bitumen felt roofing

Fig. 125

Expansion joints: Where there is an expansion joint in the structure it is necessary to form a double upstand in the roof surface to which the built-up roofing is dressed as skirtings, with the joint covered by the roofing from one side only to allow for movement of the structure and make a weatherproof joint (Fig. 125).

Laying loose-lay membrane roof coverings: The advantage of a loose-lay membrane covering to a flat roof is that as the membrane is loose it will not be subjected to the same

rupturing stresses as a fully bonded covering, due to the considerable relative thermal movements of the covering and the roof surface.

The loose-lay plasticised PVC membrane is laid loose over the roof surface with 50 overlaps at joints between sheets which are sealed by solvent welding the edges of adjacent sheets together. The exposed edge of the joint is finished with a PVC sealing mastic as illustrated in Fig. 127. To protect the membrane from wind suction uplift it is secured to the roof surface with metal discs that are

90

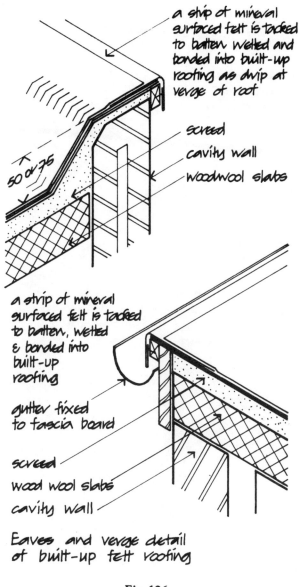

a strip of mineral surfaced felt is tacked to batten, wetted and bonded into built-up roofing as drip at verge of roof

screed

cavity wall

woodwool slabs

50 or 75

a strip of mineral surfaced felt is tacked to batten, wetted & bonded into built-up roofing

gutter fixed to fascia board

screed

wood wool slabs

cavity wall

Eaves and verge detail of built-up felt roofing

Fig. 126

screwed to the roof, with the membrane being solvent welded to the discs at the overlap joints, as illustrated in Fig. 127. At upstands the sheets are solvent welded to a plastic-coated metal profile that serves as skirting (Fig. 127).

Mastic asphalt: Asphalt is the traditional material used as a waterproof surface covering for flat roofs. The original mastic asphalt was a mixture of natural rock asphalt and natural lake asphalt.

Natural rock asphalt is mined from beds of limestone which were saturated, or impregnated, with asphaltic bitumen thousands of years ago. The rock, which is chocolate brown in colour, is mined in France, Switzerland, Italy and Germany. The rock is hard and, because of

the bitumen with which it is impregnated, it does not as readily absorb water as ordinary limestone.

Natural lake asphalt is dredged from the bed of a dried up lake in Trinidad. It contains a high percentage of bitumen with some water and about 36%, by weight, of finely divided clay.

Asphalt is manufactured either by crushing natural rock asphalt and mixing it with natural lake asphalt or more usually today, by crushing natural limestone and mixing it with bitumen, or a mixture of bitumen and lake asphalt, while the two materials are sufficiently hot to run together. The heated mixture of asphalt is run into moulds in which it cools and solidifies.

The two grades of roofing asphalt incuded in BS 988 are BS 988A, in which the asphaltic cement is 100% bitumen, and BS 988T, in which the asphaltic cement is 75% bitumen and 25% lake asphalt. The BS 988T grade in which lake asphalt is included, is easier to lay because the particles of fine clay in the lake asphalt give a smoother texture to the material than the 988A grade.

The solid blocks of asphalt are heated on the building site and the hot plastic material is spread and worked into position and levelled with a wood float in two coats breaking joint to a finished thickness of 20. The first 10 thick coat is spread on a separating layer of sheathing felt that is laid on the surface of the roof without a bond to the roof. The purpose of this layer is to isolate the asphalt from movements that will occur in the roof structure below, and also to reduce blowing of asphalt by allowing lateral escape of entrapped air and moisture that would otherwise expand and cause a blow-hole or blister on the surface of the asphalt. When the top surface of the asphalt has been finished level with a wood float and the asphalt is still hot, the surface is dressed with fine sand that is lightly rubbed into the surface with the float. The purpose of the sand dressing is to break up the bitumen-rich top surface and so avoid unsightly crazing of the top surface that would occur as the rich bitumen surface oxidised and crazed.

As the asphalt roof covering cools it gradually hardens to a hard, impermeable, continuous waterproof surface that will have a useful life of twenty years or more. In time the bitumen in the asphalt will become hard and brittle and will no longer be capable of resisting the inevitable movements that occur in any roof covering. It is practice to renew an asphalt roof covering about every twenty years if a watertight covering is to be maintained.

An asphalt roof covering is usually laid to a fall of at least 1 in 80 for run-off of rainwater to outlets.

There will be considerable fluctuations in the temperature of an asphalt roof surface that is dark coloured and absorbs radiant heat from the sun during the day and cools at night. To reduce temperature change it is practice to dress asphalt with light coloured stone chippings that reflect radiant heat, reduce heat loss at night and ageing fatigue. Stone chippings are bonded to asphalt with a

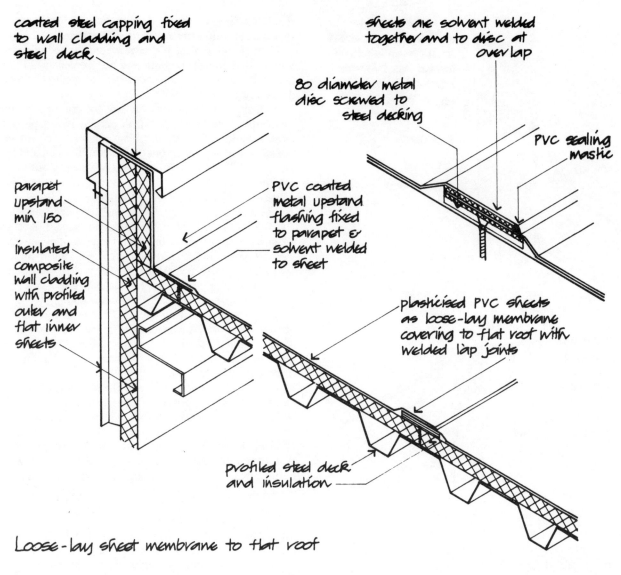

coated steel capping fixed to wall cladding and steel deck

sheets are solvent welded together and to disc at overlap

80 diameter metal disc screwed to steel decking

PVC sealing mastic

parapet upstand min 150

PVC coated metal upstand flashing fixed to parapet & solvent welded to sheet

insulated composite wall cladding with profiled outer and flat inner sheets

plasticised PVC sheets as loose-lay membrane covering to flat roof with welded lap joints

profiled steel deck and insulation

Loose-lay sheet membrane to flat roof

Fig. 127

cold applied bitumen solution.

Where an asphalt covered roof is used as balcony, terrace, promenade deck or roof garden, it is practice to add 5% to 10% of grit to the top layer of asphalt to provide a more resistant surface for balconies and terraces, and to use paving grade asphalt to a thickness of 25 for promenade decks. For roof gardens, three-coat asphalt to a thickness of 30 is used where the surface is not accessible for inspection and repair.

Asphalt is most used as a flat roof covering on solid decks of concrete and wood wool slabs and less on lightweight decks of steel and timber because of the weight advantage of built-up bitumen felt roofing. (Asphalt (20 thick): 44 kg/m^2, built-up bitumen felt roofing: 6.8 kg/m^2.)

At upstands, parapets and curbs to rooflights an upstand skirting at least 150 high is formed in one coat of asphalt 13 thick, with a reinforcing angle fillet of asphalt as illustrated in Fig. 128. The top of the asphalt skirting is turned into a groove cut in a brick joint which is finished with mortar pointing. As an additional weathering a non-ferrous metal flashing can be dressed down over the skirting from the level of the d.p.c., built into the brick parapet wall. Upstand skirtings to concrete are turned into a groove formed or cut in the concrete and the joint is finished with mortar pointing.

At verges of concrete or timber roofs the asphalt covering is reinforced with expanded metal lathing and run over the edge as a drip with three coat asphalt 20 thick (Fig. 128).

FLAT ROOFS

Curbs to rooflights are either formed in concrete up to which an asphalt skirting is run, or the curb is constructed with a pressed metal upstand with timber facing to which an asphalt skirting is formed and reinforced with expanded metal.

Rainwater outlets are usually located over points of support of the roof structure so that internal down pipes can be run either against or inside internal columns. The outlets are constructed in level valleys formed by the fall of the roof. The asphalt is dressed into the rainwater outlet as illustrated in Fig. 128.

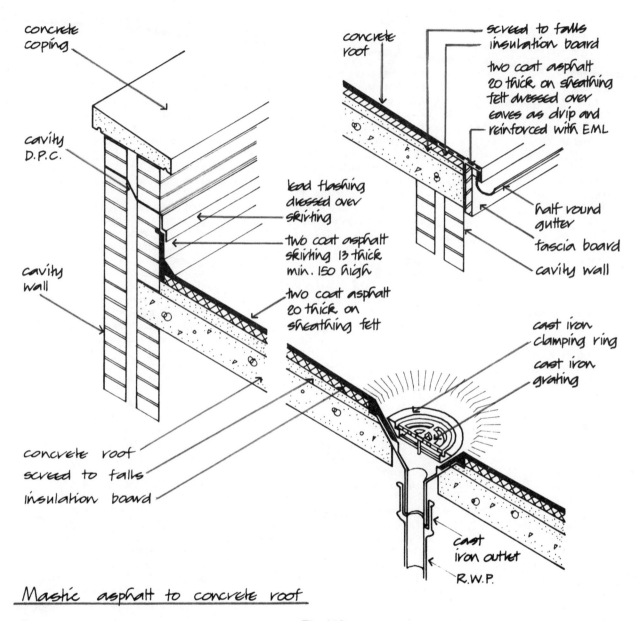

Mastic asphalt to concrete roof

Fig. 128

INDEX

INDEX

INDEX